Eyal Matsliah

Orgasm Unleashed

Your guide to pleasure, healing and power

Eyal Matsliah

First published in 2015 by Intimate Power

Cover design by Lena Kay

Disclaimer
The material in this publication is of the nature of general comment only, and does not represent professional advice. It is not intended to provide specific guidance for particular circumstances and it should not be relied on as the basis for any decision to take action or not take action on any matter which it covers. Readers should obtain professional advice where appropriate, before making any such decision. To the maximum extent permitted by law, the author and publisher disclaim all responsibility and liability to any person, arising directly or indirectly from any person taking or not taking action based on the information in this publication.

Paperback ISBN: 978-0-9944149-1-5
Ebook ISBN: 978-0-9944149-0-8

Dedication

This book is dedicated to you, dear reader.

Here's to your pleasure, healing and power!

Gratitude

My deepest gratitude goes to the many people I've encountered on my own orgasmic journey.

To Swami Vivekananda Saraswati of Agama Yoga, who introduced me to Tantric sexuality and yoga, supported me through my first years of practice and created the school and community of Agama Thailand where I lived for more than five years. Some of the important ideas and practices in this book are from Swami and Agama.

To Claudiu 'Sahajananda' Trandafir of Hriday Yoga, who showed me a spiritual path and taught me how to find who I really am beyond ego, personality and thoughts. Some of the ideas and practices he taught me found their way into this book.

To my editor Rachael Morris of Grammar Factory, who helped me turn my disjointed ideas and practices into a coherent, harmonious and beautiful book.

To my soul brother Grant Lenaarts and my blood brother Nir Mazliah, who both supported me throughout the writing process.

To Vanessa Florence, who contributed the 'unleash' part of this book's title and has greatly inspired me since the day I met her.

To Layla Martin, who believed in me as a sexual healer when I was just starting out.

To my other Tantra teachers: Ananda Maha (Mihaiela Pentiuc), Justine Baruch and Muktananda (Kushru).

To my primary school sexual education teacher, Neli Shtein.

To Sasha Cobra, Baba Dez Nicholas, David Deida, Joakim Elander, Dane Tomas, Shae Matthews, Tony Robbins, Vered Yogita Shikman and Emma Power.

To my parents Sabi and Rachel Mazliah, who bought me my first sexual education book and have believed in me even though having a son who is a sexual healer wouldn't be easy for most parents.

To all the women I have had the honor and pleasure of making love with and being with for any length of time. You have taught me so much about women, about life and about myself.

To all my private clients. Working with you has resulted in this book.

And finally, I'm grateful for being able to learn, practice and share this amazing work.

May all glory be to God.

Contents

1

How this book can change your life

The purpose of this book is to guide you in deepening and expanding your orgasmic experience, first *by yourself* and then later with your lover. The practices are designed to help you become more expressive, empowered and better connected to your femininity. Whatever stage of this journey you are at – whether you are already multi-orgasmic or have never had an orgasm – your experience of sexuality *will* transform.

An orgasm is one of the most profound states that a human being can experience. Time stops. Nothing else exists but the movement of pleasure through your body, and you feel that you are dying a sweet death but you don't mind because you are so happy and deeply fulfilled. In this state you feel connected to your body, to your deep feminine core, to your goddess essence, to your partner and to the whole of life.

Your ability to experience pleasure and orgasm is an important part of a fulfilling sex life, a meaningful relationship, and also your physical, emotional and mental health. It affects all areas of your life. And yet, many women don't experience orgasm at all, and others only experience a fraction of what's possible.

What about you? How do you experience orgasm? *Do* you experience orgasm?

The problem with orgasm today...

Society is obsessed with sex and orgasm. Women's magazines claim to teach you how to have them while men's magazines try to teach your partner how to give you one (or many).

We expect instant gratification and the mass media plays to this by providing shallow information, wrapped in bite-sized pieces of 500 words or less that promise overnight success with little or no effort. We are constantly bombarded with titles such as: '10 secrets to amazing orgasms,' '5 techniques to make her come,' '8 tips for orgasmic sex,' and more.

Yet, with this focus on tricks and tactics, we've lost something. Rather than orgasm being a sacred experience, it has been reduced to a set of 'press here to achieve this result' formulas.

And, ultimately, this disconnection with our sexual selves has led to disconnecting with others and the world as a whole.

And it's not just about sex

When I provide sexuality coaching for women, one of the first things I do is ask about their sexuality and various other aspects of their lives. A woman might tell me that her life is going well and it's only the sexual aspect that is an issue for her. But after a short discussion, we usually uncover that various aspects of her life are not going so well or are not going as well as they could. For example, she may be very creative and intelligent but can't seem to find a job that allows her to express this creativity and intelligence. Or she's successful in her business but she feels disconnected from her feminine core. Believe it or not, the root of these issues is often orgasmic, sexual or relational, and may be exactly what is holding you back in those other areas.

For many women, recognizing the connection between their orgasm or sexual issues and the other challenges in their lives is the most critical part of their orgasmic or healing journey.

Sexuality isn't something that is independent and separate from the rest of your life. It's not something you can put in a box or up on a shelf or keep hidden in a closet and just forget about. It's not a separate aspect of your life. It is an integral part of you that is connected to all other parts of you and your life. Your sex life, your connection to your body, your masculine and feminine energies, how open and expressive you are sexually, and how orgasmic you are all affect every aspect of your life – your relationship, family, studies, career, health, joy, creativity and spiritual practice.

An orgasm a day keeps the doctor away

Imagine your sex life wasn't just better – imagine it was *amazing*! How would that affect your life?

It might seem new age or clichéd to say that 'everything is connected.' But the funny thing about clichés is that they often become clichés because they are true.

Sexual energy is at the core of our being. We are created through a sexual act, we birth through a woman's vagina and our life is intimately affected by our sexuality and our sexual interaction with others. Humans are not just social creatures – we are sexual creatures. Even those who refrain from sex, such as monks and celibates, affirm its importance by avoiding it.

Sexual energy is related to your life-force energies, how much strength and vitality you have, the spring in your step and your endurance and resistance. It is closely related to your creativity, not just artistically, but also your ability to create as a mother, friend, entrepreneur or partner. It also affects how creatively you can handle life's challenges.

Sexuality is crucial for you – for your physical, emotional, mental and spiritual health and wellbeing.

Sex is not *the* most important thing in life. There is no one single aspect that is the most important thing in life. Many things are important: Health, family, relationship, financial security, having a purpose, personal and spiritual growth, making a difference, having fun and enjoying life, sexuality, and many other things. However, while sexuality is not the *most* important thing in life, it is still *one of the most important* aspects of life. It can affect all other aspects of your life, either in a disempowering or an empowering way, and it has the potential to transform those other aspects of your life as well.

So who am I to write this book?

I'm a man who writes, teaches and coaches people about sexuality. And a large part of what I teach is about female sexuality and orgasm – women's bodies, experiences and orgasmic potential.

Sometimes, people say, 'How dare a man talk about women's sexuality?' or 'How can a man relate to the experiences and sensations of a body type he doesn't have?' These are fair questions. And the short answer is: I don't know how it feels to be a woman.

However, I have worked for many years as a professional sexual healer with hundreds of women. I have studied and practiced many modalities for healing, therapy, sexuality, personal development and yoga. Furthermore, I have been teaching theories and practices that have helped women resolve sexual trauma, become multi-orgasmic, empower themselves in their femininity and sexuality, connect to their body and to their partner, and use their sexual energy to transform their lives.

I have worked with victims of rape, incest and sexual abuse as well as those with pain, irritation or anxiety around sex. Others have had deep trust issues with men.

I help women experience states of ecstasy and orgasm and guide them to reach and expand orgasm in their own practice. And it's not all physical. I also work on the energetic, emotional and mental levels. This is important because it has got a lot to do with the sexual limitations that prevent women from becoming fully orgasmic.

My work with women who are on an orgasmic journey spans three main aspects: Pleasure, healing and power. Pleasure helps you to experience the huge range of sensation and orgasmic states that are available both by yourself and with your partner. Healing helps you to move beyond trauma by dissolving blockages, dis-empowering tendencies and limiting beliefs. And power is about personal growth, helping you to become more empowered, independent and successful in all aspects of your life – personal, relationship, family, creative, social, professional, wealth and spiritual.

In the space of a few sessions, most clients are able to move beyond trauma or express emotions that have been suppressed for years. Importantly, they start to really feel pleasure. I have seen them start to shine, assert themselves and connect better with men in their communities. The changes and transformations I have witnessed in my clients have been profound.

The testimonials I receive from my clients are my greatest credentials. My female clients often say that my clarity, practicality and grounded approach have deeply served them. Please feel free to check out the client testimonials on my website (intimatepower.com).

So, although I am not a woman and would never know how it feels to be one, I have many years of study and practice, both personal and professional, to allow me to talk about female orgasm. And sometimes it's beneficial to have a totally different perspective.

What's the secret to mind-blowing orgasms?

Do you want to know the most important, easiest, most practical, best-kept secret that will instantly turn you into a multi-orgasmic woman, able to orgasm at any time, in any place, with any partner?

I hate to break it to you, but there is no such thing.

There is no one secret to great sex or mind-blowing orgasms that works for everyone every time.

You're a sensitive, perceptive and delicate being. You're also different to every other sensitive, perceptive and delicate being on the planet. This means that what worked for someone else might not work for you. What worked for you last week might not work for you today. What worked by yourself might not work with a partner. And what worked with one partner might not work with another.

Because of this, there is no single secret to great sex.

That was the bad news. The good news is...

There are *many* secrets to amazing orgasms and great sex. There are many secrets, theories, ideas, ways, techniques, exercises and practices that can help you become more orgasmic, more sensual and more in touch with your feminine core. These secrets can unlock your ability to have better sex, and harness your sexuality to become more independent, empowered and successful in all areas of your life.

Some of these secrets might be obvious; some might sound strange or challenging. Other secrets might sound unreasonable, or even impossible.

This is the nature of secrets. And this is a book of many secrets.

These secrets will be shared through a combination of theory and practices, as both are important to create lasting change. The theory part helps you understand yourself, your body and your sexuality. And the practical part helps you to embody and anchor these ideas.

The holistic transformation model

My holistic transformation model has been successful and effective in improving the lives of hundreds of people. A major part of this model is the self-work you need to do in order to change your life.

This model is comprised of five key processes:

- **Reflect** – Look at where are you now. What do you need to understand about yourself, your tendencies and your limiting beliefs? Which habits are disempowering you? What unconscious 'roles' do you play or 'stories' do you tell? How are you limiting your orgasmic experience?
- **Know** – What you need to know about your body and your capacity to orgasm. What are the twenty different kinds of orgasms you can experience? How can you become fully orgasmic?
- **Embody** – What you can actually do to embody a greater orgasmic experience and completely unleash your orgasm. Which practices will help you to overcome what is limiting you? What techniques can expand your orgasmic experience?
- **Receive** – It's okay to receive help when you need it. How can others support you in your healing? Who can assist you on your orgasmic journey?
- **Transform** –Your orgasmic practice can transform your life. What lifestyle changes will support your sexuality and orgasmic

experience? How will you express your sexual transformation in your daily life?

We start this process by looking at orgasm from different perspectives because this alone can open you up to greater orgasmic states. You might even discover that you are already experiencing some orgasmic states but haven't been aware of this. We will also see that there is one kind of orgasm that doesn't serve your orgasmic expansion.

We then examine a few different ways you can deal with any sexual issues or limitations. You might have some beliefs that are holding you back, so you will learn how to empower yourself for your own healing. Finally, we explore the powerful practices and techniques that will help you to experience new states of pleasure and orgasm. You will learn practices such as stopping yourself from orgasming, which can actually help you to orgasm better.

The five elements of holistic transformation are woven into every part of this book. As you progress, you can expect to feel more connected to your body, your femininity and your sexuality. You will become more orgasmic both by yourself and with your partner. Your daily life will become more orgasmic as well.

And more importantly – you will gain more freedom, confidence and power, because you have done it yourself! By following this model, doing your own healing work and, if needed, seeking help from others, you will be able to experience orgasm or expand your current orgasmic experience even further.

Words for the wise...

Throughout this book, we will look at orgasm in many different ways. That's one of the important things about orgasm – it is not something that can be measured, defined and labeled, but, rather, it is a vast realm that includes many different aspects, sensations, experiences, feelings, emotions, physiological phenomena, subjective perceptions, spiritual aspects and so on.

You will find contradictions throughout this book, simply because feminine sexuality isn't consistent and is constantly changing. So even when I define orgasm, take it with a grain of salt or a piece of chocolate. Adopt whichever definitions or approaches resonate with you and make you feel excited.

And while I have written this book with a heterosexual woman in mind as the reader, it can equally apply to all women, regardless of sexual orientation. If you don't identify as hetero, simply translate the gender terms I use into what serves you best.

This book is not a substitute for professional help and I am not a doctor or psychologist, so all the usual disclaimers apply. The secrets I share in this book are based on my experiences as a sexuality coach and healer. Although I draw on a lot of traditional Tantric teachings, I don't claim to represent the spectrum of Tantric philosophy. There's also a lot that I postulate and theorize about. I present my own understanding and my own blend of ideas and practices that have been beneficial in my work with female clients.

Suggestions for your orgasmic journey

Throughout this book, I will use the word vagina and yoni interchangeably. Personally, 'vagina' isn't my favorite name for the female genitalia and I prefer to use 'yoni' (pronounced yo-nee), which means 'sacred flower' or 'sacred passage' in Sanskrit – the ancient language of India. Please read these terms as your own favorite name if it is different to what I use.

I strongly suggest to you keep an 'orgasmic diary' as you progress through this book, and aim to write in it daily. You can review this diary later and see how far you have come compared to how you were when you started this process. Write what comes up for you as you read, whether you are excited because you found something that you resonate with or that helps to clarify your past experience or you read something that triggers or challenges you.

Even though some of these ideas or practices might make you uncomfortable, I suggest that you keep going with an open mind and an open heart. I know they can help you to become more orgasmic. Most importantly, I invite you to try them out and see for yourself. I suggest you use your orgasmic diary to write a short description of your experience, sensations, emotions and impressions after each practice that you complete.

In this book, you will learn a lot of different techniques that will help you to unleash your orgasmic power. In the beginning, it's important to practice the techniques (and especially the ones that challenge or trigger you). But, gradually, the techniques will become a natural part of your sexual experience and who you are.

And once you become orgasmic – and I mean *really* orgasmic – you don't need any techniques. Orgasm happens by itself. Orgasm becomes your natural state.

The fact you have chosen to read this book means you are already more open to orgasm and more willing to heal, love and empower yourself. So hang in there, do what you can and know that the best is yet to come.

Let's get started. It's time to unleash your orgasm!

Embodiment practice – Set your intentions

Intentions are powerful and setting your intentions for this orgasmic journey will be a valuable place to begin. So before you turn the page, open your orgasmic diary and note down your answers to these questions:

- In the areas of your femininity, sexuality and relationship, what are three things that challenge you?
- What are three positive outcomes that you hope to achieve by reading this book? Try to summarize this with three positive words such as 'happiness, pleasure and independence' or 'self-confidence, bliss and connection.'
- Now, have a look at your challenges and your hopes, then write down three intentions for your orgasmic journey.

Keep your intentions in mind as you read on. When you focus on your intentions, you help make them a reality in your life.

Sexual energy is creative energy. The more you stoke, unleash, express and channel your sexuality, the more you are able to create, manifest and materialize what you wish for. What have you got to lose?

I don't claim that this book can grant any wish or solve any problem, and it is not a get-orgasmic-quick scheme. Healing, change and growth take time and effort. Some of this work might be challenging, but the outcomes, benefits and rewards will be worth it.

I can't promise you that your sex and relationship will become amazing overnight. But what I suggest is that by considering the information I share and by *actually doing the practices*, your experience of your body, femininity, sexuality, pleasure and orgasm will improve. Maybe it will even radically transform. Other aspects of your life might also improve as a result.

And maybe, just maybe, this will change your life.

2

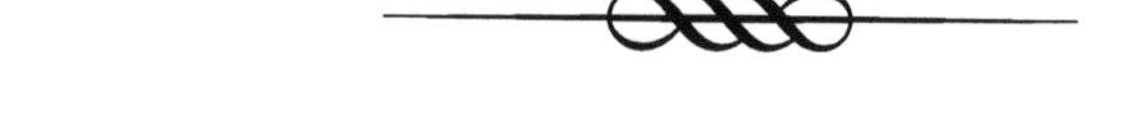

Know your orgasmic potential

Orgasmic transformation is available to everybody, whether you've never had an orgasm or you enjoy lots of them. As you learn more about the orgasmic potential within yourself, you will have already begun the process of unleashing your orgasm.

Self-reflection: *What is your understanding of an orgasm? How do you experience it?*

Most people have a limited understanding (and often experience) of what orgasm is and are, therefore, unaware of what it can be. The common understanding of orgasm is problematic. See for yourself:

'Orgasm is the sudden discharge of accumulated sexual tension during the sexual response cycle, resulting in rhythmic muscular contractions in the pelvic region characterized by sexual pleasure.' – Wikipedia

Don't you think that's a bit boring and limited?

Definitions like this are based on scientific theories that aren't aware of or won't embrace anything but the observable. But what science can't measure and can't define is where your orgasmic power lies. You see, limiting orgasm to a mere physical phenomenon robs women (and men!) of the possibility for experiencing much, much more.

My experience with my own lovers and my many clients – as well as the experiences shared by teachers, friends and students – has shown me that the common perception and experience of orgasm is only a sliver of what's possible. So I prefer to define orgasm in the following way:

Orgasm is the union of pleasure, surrender and consciousness.

The pleasure part of this is obvious. When we think about orgasm, we usually associate it with pleasure, regardless of our understanding. But surrender is an important part too. Some level of surrender and letting go is necessary to be able to experience any kind of orgasm. And the deeper you can surrender and trust, the deeper, more meaningful and more profound your orgasms will be. The consciousness part is the deep part within you that is awakened during orgasm. It's also what can take your orgasm to another level – one of personal growth and spiritual awakening.

When you expand your understanding of orgasm – your orgasm will expand.

It's important that wherever you are with your own sexuality and orgasms, you accept it for now. However, up until now you have probably been doing the same thing in order to feel pleasure and to orgasm. It's as if you've been driving the same car at night, on the same road, over and over again. You know the road, but because it's dark you don't see what's on either side of the road and you drive past the other roads that branch off from your road. Maybe this road works to get you where you are going, or perhaps you have been unwilling, unaware or afraid of exploring other roads.

This section of the book will give you a map of the orgasmic landscape so that you can experience longer, stronger and more meaningful orgasms. You will discover many different roads and look at how to better drive the vehicle of your body. It's time to reimagine the amazing vistas of what's possible and learn about the many interesting attractions and destinations that maybe you didn't even know existed.

You can regard this section as a 'philosophy of orgasm.' You will discover that there are many different kinds of orgasm and many ways to perceive them and have them. The practices I share with you in this book will help you to experience some, most or even all of these orgasms. You may even experience orgasms that I don't describe and may not even be aware of. Exploring the different approaches, definitions and types of orgasm can help you to better understand what it is and what it can be. This might seem too theoretical or 'heady' but with a better understanding, you will be better able to experience orgasm in your body.

So this section is like a guided tour, where you become more familiar with the orgasm landscape, including hands-on practices that will allow you to explore new ideas for yourself. It's going to be a fun ride!

From pleasure to orgasm

The pleasure range and orgasmic potential of women is immense. Some orgasms are focused in the genital area and last a few seconds while other deeper orgasms are felt throughout the body and can last for many minutes. Women can stay in a state of orgasm for a few minutes, half an hour or even longer – and sometimes without physical stimulation. Some women go into a state of trance, forgetting who they are and where they are, and going beyond the physical body into experiences of pure presence and bliss. The after-effects of orgasm can be felt for hours, days and sometimes weeks.

Orgasm can be experienced from nearly every part of your body. One woman might orgasm when her Achilles heel is massaged and another woman from a hand pressing on her lower belly. Others may orgasm when their ears or breasts are licked. Some women orgasm the moment they are penetrated and others by simply contracting their vaginal muscles. There are women who can orgasm with no physical stimulation at all, just by focusing their awareness on their sexual energy. And some women don't experience an actual orgasm at all, but rather go into a state of bliss during the sexual experience.

So, how do *you* experience orgasm?

Let's start unleashing your orgasm by changing the way you understand and experience pleasure.

Every pleasurable sensation is actually…

Think back to some of your best masturbation or lovemaking experiences. Maybe it was when your lover held you, touched your nipples or when he kissed and licked your yoni. And whether you orgasmed or not, you probably experienced the sensation of pleasure.

Your pleasure could have manifested in various ways: sensations or contractions in your yoni; gentle convulsions or small, involuntary body movements; jerking, throbbing or pulsating sensations; shivers or goose bumps; tingling; electric currents; heat; energy going up your spine or throughout your body; joy; or perhaps another strong emotion you felt as a sensation in your body.

When you were aware of the sensations you experienced, even for a brief moment, there was less mind activity and chatter. You were probably more connected to your body and more present in that moment. Perhaps you started to relax, let go and surrender into the pleasure. Maybe you momentarily dissolved into the sensation, or had a shift in consciousness. As if, for a split second, you forgot where you were and what was going on, and instead simply stayed present with the pleasure sensations.

Pleasure … surrender … consciousness … presence …

It sounds kind of like an orgasm, doesn't it?

Yes!

So the next time you have a sexual experience, connect to the pleasure you experience instead of worrying if you do or don't have an orgasm. The intensity of those pleasurable sensations might be light, but in quality every pleasurable sensation can be orgasmic.

Every pleasurable sensation is a mini-orgasm.

You might be asking yourself, 'Was that *really* an orgasm or was it just pleasure?' But when you perceive these sensations, these waves of pleasure, as 'just pleasure,' they will remain that – just pleasure. By giving meaning and importance to something, it can grow, expand and improve.

When you learn to recognize pleasure as orgasmic, your experience of your body, your sexuality and your orgasms will transform. You are no longer focused or dependent on a strong peak of orgasm. Instead you are able to enjoy the lightest sensation, many types of touch and any part of the sexual act because, in essence, you are always orgasmic – in a very subtle and refined way.

These pleasure sensations, or mini-orgasms, are a portal into stronger pleasure sensations. They are a pathway to stronger and longer orgasms, different kinds of orgasmic experiences and even shifts in consciousness.

Embodiment practice – Waves of pleasure

The best way to embody pleasure is to first experiment by yourself. You'll be able to stay more present with just the sensations you are experiencing this way. So this will be a self-pleasuring practice.

1. Get comfortable in a private space where you won't be disturbed and start touching yourself. Give special attention to touching, caressing and rubbing your entire body. Try using different kinds of touch, intensities, pressures, and so on.

2. Build your arousal and pleasure gradually. Bring awareness, touch and sensation to your entire body – give attention to your thighs, buttocks, belly, chest, breasts, hands, arms, neck and scalp – before you start to touch your genitals. It's important to activate your entire body so that your sexual energy doesn't stay confined to your genital area (it's like doing a warm-up before exercising).

3. Notice that you are already experiencing some pleasure. Focus on enjoying every little sensation of pleasure and celebrate it as a mini-orgasm.

4. Once you are experiencing pleasure in your body, you can begin to expand and deepen your pleasure sensations. I suggest experimenting with the following ideas:

   - Focus your mind and awareness on the sensation in your body. Visualize it: What color does it have? What shape? What texture? What smell? What taste? How does it move? How does it sound?

   - Breathe into the sensation.

   - Keep repeating the same action or touch that caused the sensations, even if they disappear for a moment.

   - If the sensation had a sound, what would the sound be? Inhale deeply and make that sound, over and over again. If you don't know what sound to make, try moaning or making a long 'aaaaaaah' sound.

   - If the sensation had a movement associated with it, what would it be? Make that movement. If you're not sure, try moving your body in different ways until it feels 'right' to you.

   - Try associating the sensations with a woman you perceive as sensual and orgasmic, either real or imaginary. How does she look? How does she move and breathe? What sounds does she make?

After you finish this practice, relax and note down all of the sensations you experienced, even when you weren't doing anything. Write this in your orgasmic diary.

This practice is a simple way to start experiencing sensation as waves of pleasure. The next time you touch yourself or have any kind of sexual interaction, bring your awareness to your sensations. Be present with whatever pleasure arises and whatever is manifesting in your body. This opens the way for more pleasure and deeper, more frequent and easier to achieve orgasms.

So you experience pleasure? Great!
You are already orgasmic.

How much pleasure is possible?

Pleasurable sensations are a big part of most orgasmic experiences, regardless of the orgasm type or intensity. In one way or another, orgasm is always a pleasure state. So one of the first ways to better understand orgasms is to discern how strong they feel and how long they last. Let's look at the range of orgasmic states that are possible:

- A wave of pleasure

  A gentle wave of intense pleasure is a mini-orgasm. It can be as simple as having your nipples touched and shivering with pleasure. For a brief moment, that sensation is all that exists. Going deeper and more fully into these waves of pleasure can create a more intense orgasmic experience.

- A mild orgasmic state

  A mild orgasmic state is made up of many small waves of pleasure. Maybe there are times during self-pleasure, foreplay or penetrative lovemaking when you don't experience a big orgasm, but rather you feel continuous waves of pleasure moving in and around your body. These sensations might originate in your genitals and then spread throughout your body or, at other times, might appear in a part of your body that is not your genitals. For example, your face or hands may become numb. The mild orgasmic state is a continuous state of arousal and pleasure, a plateau rather than a momentary peak. It is a state to aspire to – it is crucial for a woman and her partner to recognize this state so that it can be enjoyed, cherished, celebrated, explored and gradually deepened.

Many women experience this state even if they've never had an 'actual' orgasm or an orgasmic peak.

- The big 'O'

  The big 'O' is what most people, both men and women, consider to be an *actual orgasm*. I define the big 'O' as a single, strong and discernible orgasmic peak, which fades out within a minute or so. You feel intense bodily pleasure. You may also experience feelings of love, surrender, unity, serenity, peace, going beyond your body or even out of your body. Sometimes this happens to such an extent that you feel like you're about to faint. It can cause disorientation, a decreased awareness of your surroundings and the passing of time or a decreased ability – even an inability – to talk or to move. This kind of orgasm can make it difficult to have another orgasm straight away, however, we'll be looking at way you can overcome this and even expand the big 'O' into much more.

- Multiple orgasms

  A multiple orgasm is made up of successive peaks of orgasm that usually get stronger from one to the next and have intervals ranging from a few minutes to a few seconds. As you learn different orgasm practices, you will easily be able to experience many peaks instead of just one.

- Intense orgasmic state

  An intense orgasmic state is continuous and can last for many minutes, even hours. This is also known as an expanded orgasm or a plateau orgasm, as opposed to the peak orgasms we just described. This is experienced as an ecstatic, trance-like condition and some women can stay in this state with very little ongoing stimulation. After an intense orgasmic state has passed, it can take anything from a few minutes to half an hour or more to regain a normal state of consciousness and be able to function in the world, for example, walking or driving.

- Meditative orgasmic state

  A meditative orgasmic state is a very long, deep and relaxed orgasmic state. It is experienced with or without stimulation. Your breath slows considerably and your heartbeat might also slow down. You may feel inner joy, bliss, profound peace, oneness, dissolution of your personality and that 'everything is as it should be.' The physical pleasure becomes secondary compared to the feeling of bliss and transcendence. Spiritual visions, insights and realizations might also appear during this state.

- *Le petit mort*

  Le petit mort is French for 'the small death.' This is often experienced as a black out when an orgasm is so intense that you literally faint and can stay unconscious for a few minutes. This state is similar to the meditative orgasmic state but is not experienced with awareness. Compared to the other states of orgasm, this is experienced by very few women.

So, as you can see, there is a range of states that can be perceived as orgasmic. Limiting yourself to just the big 'O,' for example, does just that – limits you. The more you can recognize and experience sensation in your body, the more your orgasmic potential and subsequent experience will build.

Cultivating an orgasmic mindset

One of the basic ideas in this book is that by understanding orgasm and knowing more about it, your experience of it will change and improve, even if some of it is completely new to you.

Maybe you've never actually had an orgasm. Or perhaps you hardly ever manage to have one. Or maybe you just want more! You are not alone. Lots of women don't feel like they are orgasmic at first. You might resonate with one or more of the following experiences:

- I don't enjoy any sexual interaction with myself or with another person.
- I experience some pleasure by myself but not with another person.
- I experience some pleasure with another person but not by myself.
- I enjoy intimate touch and sexuality; I experience pleasure but I don't actually experience an orgasm.
- I get really close like I'm nearly there, on the verge of an orgasm, but it's constantly out of my reach. I either can't get there or suddenly my arousal disappears.
- I only experience orgasm very rarely and it depends on a delicate set of circumstances.

Whatever your orgasmic experience is, the practices in this book will help improve it. Even if you are crazily orgasmic, you can become even more orgasmic. Or you can start to experience different kinds and states of orgasm for the first time in your life.

Most women don't orgasm as easily and frequently as most men, either by themselves or with a partner. Many women rely on a delicate and fragile combination of circumstances in order to orgasm – the right partner, hours of foreplay and preparation, the right speed and pressure, a good vibrator, and so on. And even then it only happens sometimes. However, while a woman's orgasm isn't as automatic as a man's, it is possible to become more orgasmic.

One of the first things you can do is cultivate the right state of mind and a set of orgasmic attitudes that will help you to experience more pleasure. This then leads to deeper orgasms, both by yourself and with a partner.

Pleasure is your birthright.

I invite you to cultivate the following attitudes to help you experience more pleasure, more orgasms and a more satisfying sex life:

Relaxation

Relaxing is the single most important attitude, aspect or so-called 'technique' for orgasming. The more you are able to relax, the easier it will be for you to orgasm. Although you might be able to experience an orgasm with some effort, that tends to be a short and sharp peak, rather than a long and meaningful *state* of orgasm.

You can still explore different practices and kinds of sounds, movements, breath, and so on. But the underlying attitude is one of relaxation, not effort. Allow your actions or movements to arise naturally.

Presence and awareness

One of the most important factors in a woman's orgasmic experience is how present and aware she is while having sex with herself or with others. A man can easily orgasm even when he's not really present, perhaps even thinking about something else. But for a woman, it's crucial to be present in the moment, in your experience and in your body. Be aware of the sensations, the flow of energy, the feelings and emotions that come up and the different ways in which pleasure and orgasm are manifesting.

The more you are able to stay present, focused and aware, the more orgasmic you become. In fact, cultivating presence and awareness will affect or even transform all aspects of your life. Present moment awareness – of life energy flowing through your body, of sense perceptions, of passing thoughts – is a portal into deeper joy, sensation, pleasure, orgasm and higher states of consciousness. This is one of the ways in which sex and organism can become a spiritual experience.

Openness and detachment

Many women don't orgasm because they expect a specific experience, probably that sharp and strong peak of orgasm. They might even experience orgasmic states but simply aren't aware of that pleasure state because they are so focused on what they are expecting.

At a workshop I held in Melbourne, I facilitated a simple practice that involved partners holding hands and focusing on sexual energy together. I noticed one of the women was shaking and shivering during the exercise. After the practice, she came to me in tears. She said, 'I always thought I wasn't orgasmic. Now I understand I always have been.'

You see, orgasms come in many shapes, sizes, colors, durations and qualities. They also can include a variety of feelings, sensations, energy flows and states of consciousness. Be open to whatever happens. Whatever comes up – pleasure or pain – accept it, appreciate it and allow it to pass when it does. Don't expect a particular experience, sensation or effect. Cultivate detachment to whatever happens, or doesn't.

Patience

I've seen women sabotage their orgasm, and the whole pleasure experience, because they were so focused on and eager to get to the orgasm. Imagine a man who is focused and eager to bring you to orgasm. On the one hand, it's great that he cares, but on the other hand, it might pressure you and put an expectation on you. This can make orgasm more difficult.

Be patient and enjoy the exploration and discovery. If you don't make orgasm your goal, you may well have one anyway!

Trust and surrender

An orgasm comes from letting go and surrendering, not from control and effort. The more you can surrender to the experience, the deeper and more meaningful it will be, and it may also turn into an orgasm.

Some women stop themselves right on the verge of orgasm because they want to stay in control or they are afraid of letting go. If the idea of surrender sounds foreign to you, just try to accept and embrace whatever is happening or not happening. Allow whatever sensations, feelings, emotions or thoughts you are having, without holding on to anything. Consider saying affirmations out loud such as: 'I trust and surrender' or 'I surrender to the pleasure, the pain and whatever the moment brings.'

Courage and persistence

During your sexual explorations, both by yourself and with another, 'stuff' may come up for you. Actually, stuff probably *will* come up. You might experience physical pain, emotional pain, frustration, confusion, old memories or traumas resurfacing, or even strange physical phenomena. You could even experience pleasure that is so strong you can't contain it.

Try to cultivate the courage to first face anything that has been suppressed and then the persistence to go through it and overcome it. Remember that whatever pain or suffering you have, the benefits and positive outcomes of overcoming it will be even more powerful. It is worth facing your stuff because doing so can transform your whole life.

Enthusiasm and curiosity

It's true that facing issues around sexuality can be daunting at times, so it really helps to cultivate an attitude of enthusiasm and curiosity. Look at it as if you were exploring an unknown terrain, discovering new sensations and experiences, and meeting parts and aspects of yourself you never knew.

Try to keep a light attitude, take it easy and have fun with yourself and with others as you explore your sexuality. The more you are able to have fun with it all, the easier and more effortless it will become. Cultivate curiosity around how your body feels and functions, what's possible for you, and how the different practices change your experience day by day.

Accept the process

Life is a process. Growth is a process. Evolution is a process. Your journey of connecting to your femininity and sexuality, of healing, of becoming more orgasmic, of going deeper into meaningful relationships – is all a process.

Every step you take, everything you try, every new experience, every little win or little loss is a part of the process. Whatever comes up, whatever you experience, accept it and know that more and better is yet to come. The orgasm landscape is vast and there is a lot to explore!

The orgasm landscape

Orgasm can be experienced as a range of pleasure states; some are more continuous pleasure states and others are felt as peaks in pleasure. But there's another way to perceive these peaks and states. And a deeper understanding can help you to experience a greater range for yourself.

Imagine an orgasm landscape as a terrain full of mountains and plateaus. A peak orgasm is like the summit of a mountain. For some, it's easy to reach the peak. For others, it's difficult or impossible.

Another kind of orgasm in this landscape is more like a hill. It's easier to climb and the top of the hill has a plateau that is wide enough to stay on for a while, before coming down gradually. This is what you might experience when you are getting turned on and feeling sexual pleasure. You might already be experiencing 'hill orgasms' but not perceiving them as orgasms. Remember, if you are having some pleasure but you are discounting this as 'just pleasure,' then that is all you will experience.

Instead of having a peak moment of orgasm and ecstasy, a hill orgasm enables you to experience a state of continuous orgasm. This is milder than a peak orgasm but still very pleasurable. And what's more, it can last much, much longer. It also allows you to relax and surrender into the experience, thereby feeling it more fully. So, instead of only ever aiming for the top, for that one elusive moment of explosion, you can enjoy your pleasure as another kind of orgasmic state.

And then there is Tibet.

Tibet is surrounded by some of the highest mountains in the world, but most of its surface is a high plateau. Yet this high plain is higher than many mountain peaks. It can take some time to get to Tibet, but once you're there, you can remain up on its plateau. While it may not be quite as high as some of the mountain peaks around you, the altitude is definitely up there!

A plateau orgasm is like Tibet. It can take some time and practice to get there, but once you're there, you will experience a continuous high state of orgasm.

'I had only one orgasm ... It lasted for an hour and a half.'

So to recap, in the orgasm landscape there are generally three kinds of orgasm:

1. Peak orgasm – strong but short orgasmic moment.
2. Hill – mild but long orgasmic state.
3. Plateau – strong and long orgasmic state (aka the Tibetan orgasm).

There are techniques that can help you turn an orgasmic peak into an orgasmic state or even a plateau orgasm. And there are techniques that your partner can use to help and support you in this. We'll get to those later. For the moment, just remember that while peak orgasms are how most people define 'orgasm,' they aren't the only type of orgasm. That's not to say that peak orgasms are wrong; they can be wonderful. But it's good to be aware that they're not the only form of orgasm you can experience.

Why do we pursue the peak?

Most people experience orgasm as a short moment of maximum pleasure followed by a quick decline in both pleasure and desire. Usually, the orgasm signifies the end of the sexual interaction. This happens because orgasm is perceived as the goal of sex – the climax or peak of the experience. For some people, this peak is even the reason for sex.

Modern science has contributed to this; it defines the sexual response cycle as desire, arousal, climax and resolution. Therefore, the climax, or orgasm, is confined to one specific stage that is different to and separate from the other stages. This impacts the way orgasm is commonly perceived and experienced.

Popular culture is not without blame either. Over the past fifty to eighty years, we have seen the same scenario played out in thousands of sex scenes: The couple kiss, they take their clothes off, there is a little foreplay and then penetration. This becomes more dynamic, and they breathe and move faster and faster, finally 'coming' together in an orgasmic peak. A moment later, the man rolls over and the sexual interaction is over. We have been conditioned to perceive this as the norm.

Additionally, *men's* sexuality has influenced the pursuit of the female orgasmic peak because this is how the male orgasm is experienced. A man feels excitation that leads to an ejaculatory orgasm and resolution. After the resolution, his penis becomes soft and the passion the man feels is greatly diminished, together with his need to be connected to the woman. This can take anything from a few minutes to a few hours. But his peak usually ends the sexual interaction.

Interestingly, a woman's experience of a clitoral orgasm is very similar to a man's ejaculatory orgasm. A clitoral orgasm is usually short and sharp with the pleasure dissipating quickly. Immediately after this type of orgasm, a woman's clitoris often becomes hypersensitive and even painful to touch. This causes the woman to perceive her orgasm as a peak that has an inevitable 'valley' or decline in sensation during the resolution period.

Ultimately, peak orgasms have become the common understanding of orgasm. The problem with this is that many people perceive the orgasmic peak as the 'only' kind of orgasm or the only 'real' orgasm. There's nothing wrong with this kind of orgasm, but it's only one experience out of a vast range of possibilities. People who only focus on the peak as their goal miss out on many of the other orgasmic states that can be experienced.

Instead of looking at orgasm as a momentary peak, try to see it as a state. When you see orgasm as a state, you open the door to many different kinds of experiences that can continue for minutes, hours and sometimes days.

The power of an orgasmic state

Letting go of peak orgasm as the goal of sexual interaction will enable you to experience more orgasmic states. There are a few ways you will benefit if you choose to try this:

- Orgasm becomes an enabling state

  When you see orgasm as the goal, the sex is over when you reach it. If, instead, you see orgasm as more of a continuous state, you will enable greater pleasure in your body and a better connection with yourself and your partner. Orgasmic states can even lead to higher states of consciousness, an increased ability for manifestation (sex magic!) and, ultimately, dissolution of the ego and union with your higher self, spirit, the universe, God, or however else you like to refer to this realm.

- Orgasm becomes all-encompassing

  Most people consider orgasm to be a sexual experience, usually related to genital touch or penetration. However, it doesn't have to be only a sexual experience; it can also be non-sexual. Orgasm can be experienced without any touch and with your clothes on, either by yourself or with another person who isn't touching you.

  It's important to understand that both kinds of pleasure, both sexual and non-sexual, are an orgasmic experience. The more open you are to the idea of an orgasm being an experience you can have with or without a sex act, the more orgasmic experiences you will be able to enjoy.

- Orgasm becomes an energy source

  Peak orgasms, in particular clitoral orgasms for women and ejaculatory orgasms for men, are all about the discharge of energy and a release of tension. But an orgasmic state is experienced as something that recharges you and fills you with energy, rather than discharging your energy.

The best part about retaining your sexual energy is that you can accumulate it instead of dissipating it. With this increased reservoir of energy, you will feel more alive, more loving, more creative, more helpful towards others and more empowered in whatever you do.

As you can see, an orgasmic state offers a fair bit more than the momentary pleasure of a peak orgasm. And the beautiful thing about an orgasmic state is that it's not just longer-lasting pleasure, it is also a deeper and more meaningful experience.

Orgasmic states beyond pleasure

Most people think about sex and orgasm in the context of bodies, sexual fluids and pleasure. However, orgasmic states can be experienced as much more than just bodily pleasure. Sexual energy feels different as it builds up and expands. When you cultivate and retain your sexual energy, it will start expanding from your physical body into your energetic, emotional, mental and spiritual body or layer. This concept of our five bodies is taken from traditional yoga.

There are five kinds of orgasmic states according to the five bodies:

- Physical body – Bodily pleasure. Characterized by moaning and shouting, physical contractions, convulsions and movement. What most people consider to be pleasure.
- Energetic or subtle body – Wave upon wave of gentle pleasure sensations, sweeping your entire body. Feels less physical and more etheric, subtle or energy based. Characterized by goose bumps, shivers and a feeling of electricity flowing in or around your physical body. You might feel that your body is vibrating or humming.

- Emotional body – This is not a miniseries-style emotional drama, but a sublime and pure emotional expression of unconditional love, compassion and surrender. In this state, you realize that bodily pleasure, as great as it is, has its limits when compared to the experience of deep and all-encompassing, unconditional love.
- Mental body – An experience of deep presence, awareness and laser-like perception. Characterized by mental clarity and void of 'noise.' Everything becomes clear and quiet. Thoughts might appear but quickly dissolve.
- Spiritual or causal body– In very special instances, you can experience a type of transcendence. You might feel eternal and in union with your higher self, with the divine and with the universe. You feel deep reverence and sacredness and might become aware of your spiritual calling.

You might wonder how these last two states – mental and spiritual – could be considered pleasurable or orgasmic. That's a good question. Has your mind ever been bothered by an endless stream of thoughts, emotions, worries or fears? If so, you will recognize that the experience of pure presence and a mental void would actually be a relief and very pleasurable. And the experience of transcendence and oneness is orgasmic because it is the deepest experience of bliss, and one that transforms lives.

This is the idea behind sexual Tantra and sacred sex – that sexual energy can start with the body and then use pleasure to go beyond the body and into the spirit. And the best thing is that you are encouraged to experience and enjoy all of these states.

Experience more from your orgasm

If you would like to experience more from your orgasm, you'll need to explore different practices to those you have always relied on.

This means discovering ways to feel orgasmic pleasure that are not dependent on your clit.

Self-reflection: *After an orgasm, does your clit feel overly sensitive or do you ever feel unsatisfied or depleted?*

Most people understand the clitoris to be the small pea-shaped part of the vulva, tucked under the clitoral hood and above the urethra and vaginal opening. But research shows that this is *just the tip*; the clitoris actually extends throughout the female genitalia and envelopes the vagina. Subsequently, there are theories that say there is only one kind of orgasm – a clitoral orgasm – and that clitoral stimulation is necessary to achieve orgasm. However, my experience with many female clients, as well as the experience of my teachers and colleagues, shows otherwise.

Clitoral orgasms are just the beginning

Many young girls first experience orgasm through masturbation. They might touch their genitals with their hands or rub up against a toy or a pillow, which stimulates their clitoris and can result in an orgasm. As they grow up, many women continue to focus on their clit even when they begin to explore penetrative sex.

> *'The only drawback to masturbation is that I can reach climax so quickly – and then it's a major letdown.'*

Let's be clear here, clitoral orgasms are not a bad thing. There isn't anything wrong with them or with you enjoying them. That being said, what I do invite you to consider are these questions:

- If there are so many other types of pleasure and orgasm states, why would you *only* want to have clitoral orgasms?
- Would you like to be able to choose what type of orgasm or orgasmic state you feel like experiencing?

- What if clitoral orgasms have some side effects that don't always serve you?

Think back to the last time you masturbated. Let's assume it was one of those times that you were mainly focused on stimulating your clit. Now ask yourself this:

- After the orgasm, was your clit hypersensitive? Was it even uncomfortable or unbearable to touch?
- If you had the time to continue pleasuring yourself, why did you stop?
- Even though you experienced pleasure and release, did you feel deeply satisfied?

Let's generalize for a moment and see if the following description is similar to your experience of a clitoral orgasm:

First of all, to orgasm in this way there needs to be some kind of effort. A clitoral orgasm is then most likely to manifest as an intense, short and sharp peak. The build-up is usually fairly quick – some women can reach a clitoral orgasm in a minute or two – and the orgasm itself is brief, lasting for about twenty to thirty seconds. The pleasure sensations and the orgasm are mostly focused in the genital area.

During or immediately after the peak of the orgasm, the clitoris becomes hypersensitive and any touch feels irritating or 'too much.' It might feel annoying, uncomfortable or maybe even painful. Perhaps you have found yourself saying something like this to your partner: 'Lay off my clit, *now.*' If your clit becomes hypersensitive, you probably had a clitoral orgasm and this is the best way to differentiate between a clitoral and a vaginal orgasm. The clitoral orgasm is followed by a quick decline in pleasure, arousal and interest in further stimulation. Some women need to wait a few minutes or sometimes hours before they are ready for more clitoral touch, or for another clitoral orgasm.

If you are with a partner, the orgasm will feel like 'my orgasm' rather than an ongoing and shared state. You might lose interest in some way, still loving your partner, but somewhat less interested to share with them in that moment compared to how you felt before the orgasm. Note, this is similar to how a man feels after an ejaculation. There is some satisfaction in the release of energy, but it's more like the goal's been achieved or you've ticked the orgasm box. Then it's on to the next thing.

Clitoral orgasms don't really offer a lasting and deep level of satisfaction. Some women have said they even feel hollow, depleted, dull, unfulfilled, frustrated or even slightly depressed after this type of orgasm. Perhaps you have experienced some of these effects. But why is the orgasm so short and sharp? Why does your clit feel pleasurable one moment and then unpleasant to touch the next? Why do you sometimes feel depleted, unsatisfied or even frustrated afterwards?

Explosive orgasms – not what you thought they were

A clitoral orgasm is an explosive orgasm because the accumulated sexual energy is exploded downwards, out of your body. In brief, during an explosive clitoral orgasm you lose energy, while in other kinds of orgasms you can retain and circulate that energy.

The ancient science of Tantra offers an interesting explanation for this kind of energy. It suggests that the energy is accumulated in the genital area during sexual stimulation, and specifically in the second (sacral) chakra. So the pleasure will be perceived mostly in the genital or pelvic area. Stimulating the clitoris causes the energy to be volatile and creates a downward flow of energy. It might even feel 'heavy,' 'stagnant' or 'sticky.'

When you orgasm, you lose the energy that you just created during stimulation. This loss of energy is what creates the hypersensitivity of the clitoris and is why some women feel a bit depleted or might take a few minutes or hours before they can orgasm again. It's also why you might feel unsatisfied on a deeper level.

> *'I feel that I definitely got slightly addicted to clitoral orgasms and would turn to that as a form of release (especially after internal stimulation didn't cause me to orgasm). I am now quite strict about not resorting to this as I do feel that it makes me more moody and up-and-down emotionally.'*

Furthermore, sexual energy is life-force energy, and when you have frequent clitoral orgasms of the kind described earlier, your energy is drained and you are deprived of that power source. This energy is what makes you stronger, more independent, empowered, creative and successful. Having frequent clitoral orgasms can even cause you to menstruate longer and heavier, with stronger side effects. This is because your body has been 'trained' to release and expel energy instead of retaining and circulating it.

A clitoral orgasm is usually a peak orgasm and similar to a man's ejaculatory orgasm. A man's ejaculatory orgasm is also an explosive orgasm because his sexual energy is released and expelled from his body in the form of sperm. A man will become aroused quickly, his orgasm is brief (even shorter than a woman's clitoral orgasm) and he immediately enters the refractory period. He loses his erection and also loses at least some interest in continuing to engage with his partner. Have you noticed that men don't just lose their erection but also their arousal, their presence and their connection with you? Falling asleep is not uncommon here. I'm sure you have experienced this! A woman's energy does a similar thing after a clitoral orgasm.

> *'I agree that external clitoral-only orgasms do leave me feeling depleted.'*

Let's visualize it this way: Think of a pressure cooker. It's much faster to cook something in a pressure cooker because of the intense pressure and heat locked inside the pot. It's a kind of energy, like your sexual energy. Now imagine the pressure cooker is faulty and that once the pressure is built, the lid flies off. All of the steam discharges and the contents of the pot spill everywhere. That's kind of what happens with an explosive orgasm.

But imagine cooking a delicious soup in your pressure cooker where, instead, you keep the lid on even once the soup is cooked. It will stay hot and ready for hours after you turn the heat off.

> *'I have only had explosive clitoral orgasms and was always left feeling like I was missing something.'*

There is another kind of orgasm

If you thought clitoral orgasms were fun, you're in for a treat!

A vaginal orgasm is very different. Rather than using clitoral stimulation, a vaginal orgasm is usually experienced by stimulating the G-spot, the walls of the vagina and the cervix (the entrance to the womb). In comparison to an *explosive* clitoral orgasm, an orgasm that comes from vaginal stimulation is usually an *implosive* orgasm. The sexual energy is imploded, retained and then circulated within your body. These orgasms can last for long minutes and even hours, because as long as you are retaining your energy, you are able to use it to orgasm again.

This kind of orgasm is attained and experienced as a type of 'releasing,' 'allowing,' 'letting go' and 'surrendering.' Compared to a clitoral orgasm, which is often experienced as a kind of 'effort,' 'trying' or 'grasping' – the vaginal orgasm is felt as deep satisfaction and relaxation.

You'll know when you have a vaginal orgasm because it feels totally different. The build-up is slower; it takes longer to get aroused and you'll need more time for stimulating your whole body and then your vagina. Some women need up to an hour of foreplay and penetration before they orgasm in this way. The orgasm itself also unfolds slower and lasts longer (sometimes much, *much* longer). During and after this orgasm, you can continue to receive stimulation and the clitoris doesn't become oversensitive. Another orgasm is possible within minutes or even seconds.

If we are thinking about the landscape of an orgasm, this one feels like a 'dome' rather than a 'peak.' The pleasure feels more intense because it is deeper and fuller; it's expansive, all-encompassing and meaningful. Even though the stimulation might originate in the genital area, the pleasure often emanates and spreads in waves throughout the whole body. This usually moves towards the upper areas of the body but also downwards, hence the term 'toe-curling orgasm.'

But it's not just about pleasure and orgasm. The surrender into a vaginal orgasm feels meaningful and special. You may feel greater love and connection – with yourself, your partner, your life and sometimes with the universe.

You will probably need to feel trust and connection with the person you're with to orgasm in this way. If you are with a partner, your orgasm will feel like 'our orgasm' instead of 'my orgasm.' It's like a gift you want to share, not an achievement you want to keep.

During the hours and days following a deep vaginal orgasm, you might sometimes feel echoes of that orgasm in the form of vibrations, pulsations, sustained pleasure in your body or feelings of love and bliss.

And there's even more.

While clitoral orgasms can deplete your life-force energy and your ability to be creative, vaginal orgasms empower you as a woman. They charge your body, spark your creativity, fuel your confidence and can inspire success in your career. This kind of orgasm is nourishing for your body and soul. And, at its best, it connects you to your own feminine essence, to your partner, to others and to life.

Women who experience deep vaginal orgasms usually prefer them to clitoral orgasms, because they feel better – physically, emotionally, energetically and spiritually. *(see Diagram 1 on page 40)*

> *'I have been practicing implosive orgasms and I'm surprised at how easy it is. I always thought I wouldn't manage so I just put up with clitoral orgasms. But I have to say, implosive orgasms are much more satisfying and now I feel like having sex every day. At the moment I just practice with myself but that's okay ... I'm still happy!'*

Explosive vs. Implosive Orgasm

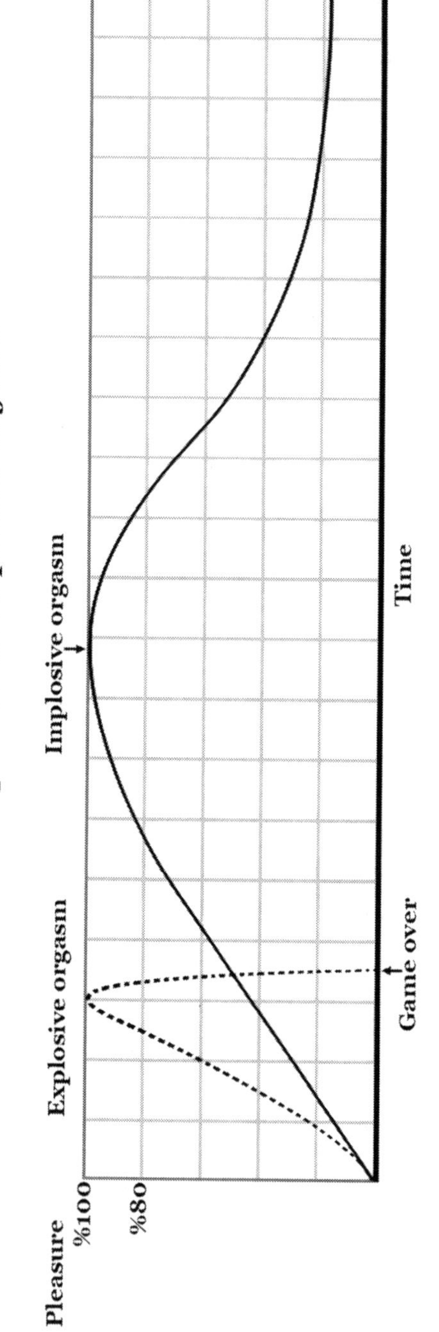

Diagram 1

Unfortunately, most women and men have been led to believe that the clitoris is the only sensitive area in a woman's body and that clitoral stimulation is necessary to achieve orgasm. The clitoris is easy to find, easy to arouse and easy to orgasm from. So it's been clit, clit, clit, clit, clit, clit and more clit. In comparison, experiencing a vaginal orgasm is a bit more challenging. It takes much more openness, willingness and surrender on the part of the woman. It also requires patience, experience and persistence on the part of her partner.

> *'I'm experiencing the difference between a clitoral orgasm and a longer, intense, deeper internal orgasm. The level and type of energy is different and during the days after, I still have this nice sexual, female energy in and around me. So good!'*

The clitoris is a sacred, beautiful, crucial part of a woman's body and sexuality. But it's not the only part. There is a vast, uncharted, blissful world in there – in your vagina – waiting to be explored and yearning to be honored, celebrated and unleashed!

Moving beyond clitoral orgasms

Clitoral orgasms involve local and superficial sensations that are usually followed by a quick decline in pleasure and a period where you are unable to receive further clitoral stimulation. So it's important to note that certain positions stimulate the clitoris more than others. For example, during penetrative sex when either partner is on top and leaning forward, it can over-stimulate the clitoris and lead to a clitoral orgasm.

But what if you could receive intense and prolonged vaginal *or* clitoral stimulation – enjoy those sensations – and then turn them into meaningful and empowering states of whole-body orgasm? Would you be interested in trying?

Well, it is indeed possible, and you will be able to do this within a few days of practice. And most women never look back once they have learned to expand and extend their orgasm. It's like having the best of both worlds – enjoying the ease and strong sensation of clitoral stimulation as well as the longer, deeper and more meaningful experiences of a vaginal orgasm.

To discover the ecstasy and bliss of continuous vaginal or internal orgasms, it's important that you avoid having a clitoral orgasm for a while. However, after you learn how to turn clitoral stimulation into an internal orgasm, you will be able to enjoy clitoral stimulation while avoiding an explosive clitoral orgasm.

If moving beyond clitoral orgasm is something you desire, you'll need to learn how to explore the orgasm landscape with a bit more expertise. And the best place to start is at your 'point-of-no-return.' Let's call this the PNR.

The point-of-no-return

The PNR is the exact point at which arousal turns into a peak orgasm. This creates a cascade of physiological responses, a bit like an avalanche in the landscape. It triggers a series of vaginal contractions that scientists love to quote as the primary sign of orgasm. There is also a strong release of neuro-transmitters in the brain and hormones in your body that cause the momentary sensations of pleasure, euphoria and joy. The other side of these natural chemicals is that they also cause mood swings and emotional effects that can last up to two weeks before they stabilize. This is especially so following an explosive clitoral orgasm.

It is crossing the PNR that leads to experiencing an orgasm as a short and sharp peak. As we discussed earlier, this is how most people define and experience orgasm. But you can experience orgasm in other, more powerful ways if you choose. And if you can identify your PNR, you can work with it.

The best way to become attuned to your PNR is to begin playing with it during your self-pleasuring practice before moving on to partner exploration. When you are pleasuring yourself by arousing your clit, notice if you experience any of the following sensations:

- Your breath becomes faster, more shallow and constricted.
- You feel compelled to tense your body and tighten your muscles.
- Your entire attention is focused on your genital area.
- Your movements become more mechanical.
- Your genital area is charged in a 'sharp' or 'heavy' way.
- Your pleasure is rising and increasing very quickly.
- You feel the desire to apply even more stimulation.
- You feel compelled to push down and out with your vaginal muscles (also known as 'bearing down').
- You feel a sense of urgency to 'come.'

That moment when you feel the need to 'come,' to rush or to tense up is the moment just before the PNR. Once you cross that point, you will usually have a peak orgasm, and it will probably be an explosive clitoral orgasm. However, these short and superficial orgasms are stopping you from experiencing longer, ecstatic orgasmic states.

So, if crossing the edge of the orgasmic cliff creates the cascade and avalanche, what do you do instead?

You don't cross the edge. You pause.

When I started exploring Tantric sex and sexual healing many years ago, I used to be very dynamic, active and intense. Then I discovered that if I paused while making love or when stimulating a woman's yoni, she often had a response such as crying or orgasming. It's as though she thought the lovemaking was over and finally allowed herself to relax and let go. The pause allowed her to express her emotions or allowed the sexual energy to turn into an orgasm.

So when you self-pleasure or have sex, pause for a minute every ten minutes or so. Become present with the sensations in your body, your feelings and emotions. Connect with your partner via your eyes, breath, soft words or touch. Then resume what you were doing earlier. This is a particularly good thing to do when you near your PNR.

Embodiment practice – Edging

There is a technique called 'edging,' which can also be understood as 'do not orgasm!' It's an excellent technique that can either turn clitoral stimulation into internal orgasm or a single orgasmic peak into a longer orgasmic state.

Again, it's much easier to learn this by yourself before you attempt it with another person, since you have more control over the stimulation. It's practiced in the following way:

1. Start to self-pleasure and gradually make your way towards your yoni. Use lots of oil to massage your pubic mound, your outer and inner lips and your clitoris area. Build your pleasure gradually, while breathing, moving and making sounds.

2. Be aware of any of the telltale signs of your impending PNR. Notice that there will be a moment when the pleasure or energy starts to feel very sharp, as if it's rising quickly. You might feel compelled to apply even more stimulation, to tense your body, to tighten your muscles, to breathe faster or to bear down. You feel that you *want* to, you *need* to, you *have* to come!

3. DON'T!

   If you do, you will probably have a clitoral orgasm, which might be pleasurable but will prevent you from learning how to internalize your clitoral stimulation. And you need to be able to do this if you want to turn short peaks of orgasm into long orgasmic states.

4. Instead, just stop all of the stimulation and completely relax your body. You can be close to the PNR but make sure you stop stimulating yourself before this point. Before it's too late.

5. Take slow and deep breaths, with extra-long exhalations. The main thing you need to do now is to move your sexual energy away from your genitals. To do this, try touching other parts of your body or taking a break.

6. When you feel that your pleasure has subsided a bit, you can resume your stimulation. Once again, build your arousal and pleasure until you are right back in that zone just before the PNR – then relax again.

7. Keep doing this for at least twenty minutes, and preferably for an hour or more. You want to be able to constantly 'edge' yourself close and then stop on the verge of orgasm.

If, during this practice, your clit suddenly became hypersensitive and unpleasant to touch or if you suddenly lost interest in your practice, you probably had a clitoral orgasm. That's okay. When you feel ready, arouse yourself again, this time stopping *well ahead* of your PNR. *(see Diagram 2 on page 46)*

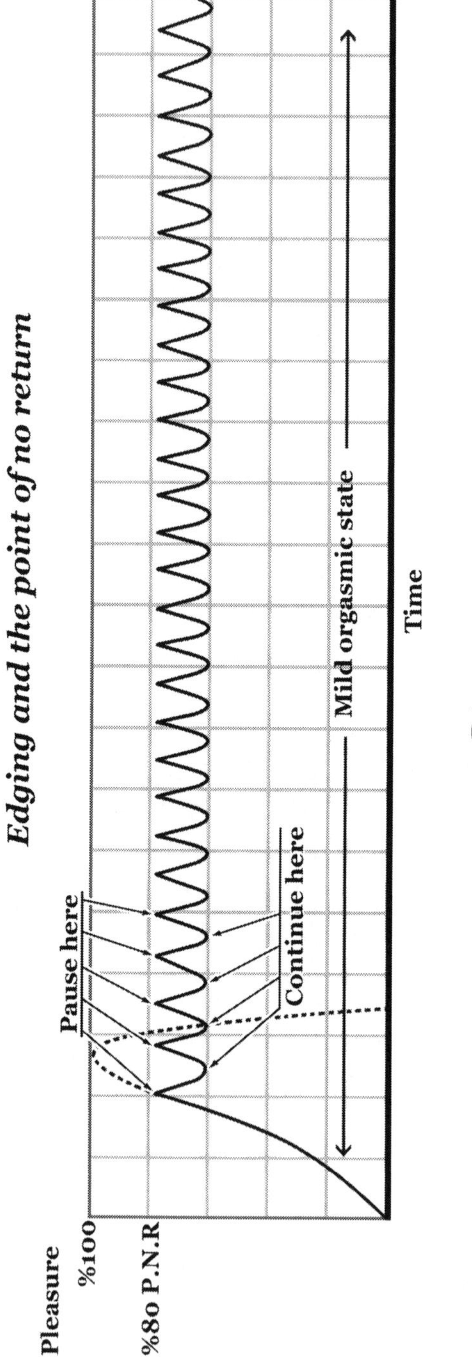
Edging and the point of no return
Pleasure
%100
%80 P.N.R
Pause here
Continue here
Mild orgasmic state
Time

Diagram 2

After a while of enjoying this practice, you might come to realize that, instead of having an orgasmic peak, you have been in an orgasmic state all along. In the beginning, it might feel like 'just pleasure,' but after doing this practice for a week or two and after half an hour of stimulation, you will start to recognize that what you are feeling is much more than 'just pleasure.' The build-up of sexual energy in this practice creates an orgasmic state, which you can feel even after you stop touching yourself. You may even have an internal orgasm. Surprise! Your orgasmic power is expanding already.

Good things come to those who wait. And those who wait – come.

And there are plenty of techniques you can try out that can help you to move beyond explosive clitoral orgasms and into the range of implosive internal orgasms.

Turning clitoral stimulation into an internal orgasm

Being able to stop yourself from experiencing a peak clitoral orgasm is the first step to cultivating a deeper and more internal orgasm. Once you can do that, you can use a variety of techniques to spread your sexual energy to other parts of your body and increase the pleasure sensations inside your vagina.

Let's look at a few techniques you can try now:

- **The pause** – Every few minutes during stimulation, pause completely. Relax your breathing and your body and stop any movement. Allow your arousal to decrease before continuing. This is a powerful technique that you can use while self-pleasuring, having foreplay, having sex or any other activity. It increases your awareness and moves you from 'doing' pleasure to 'being present' with pleasure.

- **Finger tracing** – Move your fingers from your clitoris and down into your vagina. Curl your finger upwards, towards your pubic bone and press there. Repeat this movement. It moves the pleasure and sexual energy away from your clitoris and into your vagina, bringing awareness, sensation and pleasure. It's a great way to awaken and activate your G-spot and it also creates a new neurological pathway between this area and your clitoris.
- **Internal stimulation** – One of the best ways to move sexual energy into your vagina is by applying internal stimulation. You can do this with a dildo or, if you don't have one, consider a penis-shaped vegetable. Try applying both clitoral and internal stimulation at the same time, while keeping your focus inside your vagina. Gradually, apply more internal stimulation and less external stimulation, until you are hardly touching your clit at all and you can feel the pleasure increasing internally.
- **Internal awareness** – Focus your awareness inside your vagina. Be aware of any warmth, tingling, vibrating, pulsating, throbbing or any other sensation, even if it's numbness. Do this continuously, and specifically when you use 'The pause.'
- **Breath and sound** – Keep breathing fully into your belly, focusing on your exhale and making a long 'Ahhhh' sound as you breathe out.
- **Movement** – It's also important to allow your whole body to move, twist and undulate. In particular, allow your hips to undulate back and forth, side to side and in circles. Let this movement expand to your spine, shoulders, head and your entire body. This builds sexual energy and pleasure and also allows the sexual energy to spread into your entire body.

- **Spread it** – Keep caressing your entire body and consciously move your hands away from your genital area and towards other parts of your body, specifically your upper body. Imagine that you are spreading and moving your sexual energy – as if it's a lump of butter that you are spreading over toast.
- **Touch** – Explore different kinds of touch all over your body – caress, pull, squeeze, twist, pinch, press, stroke, fondle, brush, knead, massage and slap. Experiment with different sensations – you might be surprised at what feels good!
- **Visualization** – Visualize a stream of light, heat, electricity or energy following the path that your finger traces from your clitoris into your vagina (see 'Finger tracing'). And beyond the vaginal orgasm, you can also visualize this energy travelling up your spine and emanating from the top of your head. This leads to another type of orgasm that we'll be looking at later.
- **Squeeze** – While stimulating your clit or during the pauses, contract and relax your vaginal muscles in rhythmic repetitions. This brings awareness and sensation into your vagina, and helps you move the sexual energy up your spine. Experiment with different kinds of squeezes – short, long, pulling in, squeezing tightly and even pushing out.

  Some women habitually 'push out' their vaginal muscles, which causes an explosive orgasm or just a loss of sexual energy. If your clit becomes hypersensitive, it might mean that you had an explosive orgasm. Some level of alternate pushing out and pulling in is pleasurable and beneficial; it's just important that you do not push out too much and lose your orgasm in this way.
- **Affirmations** – Affirm your orgasmic power to yourself. Say, either out loud or internally, something like, 'My sexual energy is flowing into my vagina' or 'My whole body is orgasmic.' Consider writing your affirmation down and placing it where you will see it often, such as on your laptop, mirror or fridge.

I encourage you to give some of these techniques a try. Experiment for a few weeks and record your experience in your orgasmic diary. Discuss your experience with female friends who have internal orgasms and know the difference. And don't worry if you occasionally explode into a clitoral orgasm. Just build your pleasure again and keep going.

Orgasmic extras

There are also ways that your partner can support you in this practice. Check out the resources section of my website for more detail (www.intimatepower.com/orgasm-book-resources).

You might be used to having quick and easy clitoral orgasms, and maybe you once believed that's all there was. But after a few days or, at most, weeks of practice, you will be able to receive more and more clitoral stimulation and be able to transform it into prolonged internal or whole-body orgasms.

Try to practice this for at least thirty minutes every day, where you are stimulated but don't reach a clitoral orgasm, either by yourself or with your lover. The idea is to build up enough energy that it starts emanating throughout your whole body and, later, into your life. This will be the best homework you ever get!

> *'I had no idea about this, but it worked! I had lots and lots of goddess spot orgasms. First time ever. Beautiful. I cried a lot. It was so easy, but nobody ever told me how.'*

If you're ready to explore a more orgasmic state and different types of orgasm, then it's time to get intimate with the most important person on your orgasmic journey.

3

Reconnecting with yourself

Now that we know a bit about orgasms, it's time to go deeper. It's time to meet the most important person on your orgasmic journey – you.

In this section of the book, you will reconnect with yourself – your yoni, your juices, your pleasure and your body. You will discover why pleasuring yourself is so important to your orgasmic journey and new ways to do this. You will experience your yoni in new ways and see that connecting to her allows you to embrace your femininity. Importantly, you will be invited to accept yourself as you are and also to allow yourself to change and grow, like a flower.

Self-reflection: *How deeply do you love and accept your body?*

Self-love and acceptance are important on your orgasmic journey. And it's not just accepting your sexuality and your sexual organs, you need to love and accept your whole body. To say 'yes' to being orgasmic, you first need to say 'yes' to yourself.

Your attitude towards your body affects how much you enjoy sex and how much others will be attracted to you. If you don't like your own body and radiate that energy, how can you expect others to love it for you? They pick up on how well you accept yourself and take the lead from you.

I have seen women who are overweight and would not be considered particularly attractive by modern standards. But when these women have loved, adored and cherished their own bodies, it has made them attractive in the eyes of the people around them. I have had a few lovers like this and it is a pleasure and an honor to be with someone who is confident in their body, regardless of what the sought-after norm might be.

Marilyn Monroe is considered to be one of the biggest sex symbols in history. However, if you analyze her face according to common standards of female beauty, you will find that it was asymmetric and slightly disproportionate. There were many Hollywood actresses who were more 'beautiful' than Marilyn. But her charisma and sensuality made her a legendary beauty.

On the other hand, there are the women who are very beautiful according to modern standards. Yet, often, when I encounter these women, they don't really like their own body and keep finding (and voicing) perceived faults. As a result, men who would normally be attracted to them because of their good looks get turned off because their beauty is like a shell that holds an unattractive woman inside. Their lack of self-acceptance affects the people around them.

Today, weight is one of the biggest issues women struggle with when it comes to self-acceptance. In western society, obesity is an epidemic and is not a healthy state for your body. On the other hand, modern standards of beauty depicted through fashion, advertisements and celebrities promote much thinner body weights than a normal healthy weight. As a result, women grow up and live with impossible standards of beauty, which has led to more teenagers and young women developing eating disorders than ever before.

Being too overweight can affect your orgasmic ability because your health is affected. And aiming to be super thin can also affect you because being underweight can rob you of some of your orgasmic ability. However, it's not just about weight.

It's about all aspects of female beauty. The fashion industry used to spend hours and hours on make-up and hairstyling to improve the looks of the models and hide their many human imperfections. But now, in addition to all of that, photo-editing software is used to manipulate women's features even further. The final photo used in the media more often than not looks very different to the woman who posed in front of the camera. And it's not just skin blemishes that are digitally erased; entire body proportions are being reshaped. These photos present ideals of beauty that are unrealistic and cause a distortion in our collective perception of beauty.

You are probably already aware of this. Yet, in spite of your awareness, you are probably still affected by these unnatural and impossible depictions of female beauty. Perhaps you still judge yourself for not looking like those images. So, what is your attitude towards your body? Are you comfortable in a bikini on the beach? Are you comfortable being naked? Do you prefer to turn off the lights when you're having sex? Do you love your body?

Look at yourself naked in the mirror and find all the things that you *do* love about your body. There will always be things that you don't like, so focus on the things that you do like. Aim for a healthy weight rather than the 'ideal' body based on unrealistic images in the media. If you want to support your orgasmic journey, you need to accept and love your body. And one way you can express your love and acceptance is to gift yourself with regular self-pleasure.

Pleasure yourself

I said earlier that there is no one secret to great sex because there are many secrets. But if I had to choose the most powerful one, this is it. Obviously, we're talking about masturbation here. But even the word masturbation can have negative connotations for some. It might be regarded as something that you do when you don't have a partner or if your partner doesn't satisfy you. In particular, women masturbate less often than men and are less likely to admit to doing it.

Self-reflection: *How comfortable are you with touching yourself? How often do you do it?*

Masturbation is the most basic and natural sexual behavior. Even fetuses in the womb have been shown to pleasure themselves in this way. Perhaps you have noticed how often kids touch their genitals or rub themselves on pillows, furniture or toys? It's completely normal. However, it's very common for parents who witness a young boy or girl masturbating to either reproach them or punish them. Even if the parent doesn't say anything, their energy changes and children are very perceptive to these shifts. So they start believing that they have done something 'wrong.'

When adults react towards a young one's masturbation with these attitudes, they lay the first foundations of guilt and shame around masturbation. This also extends to body image, sexuality and one's feminine or masculine essence.

I've worked with many women experiencing sexuality issues and I've noticed a few common things:

- Some women have guilt and shame around masturbation and aren't comfortable doing it.

- Other women don't take full pleasure in their masturbation. Or they only do it in a mechanical and superficial way, perhaps as a quick fix or a sleeping aid.
- Many women are overly focused on clitoral stimulation, missing out on the vast range of experiences, sensations and orgasmic states possible for them.
- And some women get attached or addicted to their vibrator. This can cause their yonis to become desensitized or numb, and even make it difficult to experience pleasure with a partner because no man can produce the same stimulation that a vibrator does.

Maybe you have some of these tendencies or experience some shame or inhibition around masturbation as well.

Imagine, for a moment, going to visit someone's house for the very first time. You want to be shown around by them and introduced to the environment. But they aren't really sure where each room is or where the light switches are or how to operate the heating or cooling. They keep stumbling into things and don't seem comfortable within their own home. How do you think it feels to be a visitor in their home?

Now, imagine your body is a house, mansion or temple, if you like. When you invite someone in, do you know your body-temple well enough to guide others through it? Are you able to show them how to engage with your home?

I'm sure you've experienced a lover who doesn't know what they're doing or doesn't know how to touch and pleasure you. Maybe they touch you too harshly or too softly or reach for your yoni too early. Even worse, have you been with someone who is not present and connected with you? But it's not just about your visitor. They usually learn how to be in your environment based on how *you* are in your environment and how *you guide them*. So the better question is, do you know how to touch and pleasure yourself in the way you want to be touched and pleasured?

The secret to great sex is learning how to have great sex with yourself!

There are so many ways of masturbating and so many reasons to, including:

- You become more connected with your body, your yoni, your femininity and your sexuality.
- You can experience different kinds of pleasure and orgasm states.
- You can discover and awaken more erogenous zones in your body.
- You can heal yourself from pain and trauma.
- You become independent and empowered in your sexuality, not needing someone else to fix, pleasure or fulfill you.
- You can find the inner union of masculine and feminine energies with your self-empowering and self-affirming practice.
- You can raise your sexual resonance and, as a result, attract better lovers.
- When you know how to pleasure yourself, you can teach your partners how to better pleasure you.
- You can use your sexual energy to charge up your health, creativity, career, relationships and spirituality.

Good things come to those who masturbate.

As a sexuality coach, masturbation is the core practice that I invite my clients to either begin or explore with a new perspective. And this suggestion applies whether they are in a relationship or not. For some women, it can be challenging at first. It might feel mechanical, superficial or even alien. But after a few days of daily practice, or at most two weeks, they start to feel the positive effects. You can become significantly more orgasmic from this practice alone.

Masturbation is one of the most important sexual activities that you can do. It has an effect on your physical and emotional health, your orgasmic ability, your enjoyment of sex and even how you live your life. If you don't understand your own sexual pleasure, how can anyone else possibly work it out?

So, as a start, instead of calling your practice masturbation, try to think of it as self-sex, self-love or self-pleasure. Use whatever word resonates with you and excites you. Your masturbation practice and your experience of orgasm can be transformed when you focus on cultivating self-pleasure.

Orgasmic reminders

There are a few things to remember before beginning your self-pleasure practice. These reminders will help you to experience pleasure and will make it easier for you to orgasm.

First, the most important reminder:

Pleasure = Orgasm.

Remember to recognize every small sensation of pleasure as a mini-orgasm. Gradually, these waves of pleasure will expand into your full orgasmic experience.

Next, let's cover some approaches that will support your pleasure practice.

Take your time

Allow yourself plenty of time to build your pleasure and experience your orgasm. Some men can come in thirty seconds (and you may have met some that were even faster). But women can sometimes take half an hour to an hour to reach a deep and meaningful orgasmic state. And it's not just about a single experience; the journey to deeper orgasms can take months or even years.

Take your time and enjoy the orgasmic experience you are having right now, knowing that best is yet to 'come.'

Create the space

The environment you create for yourself matters. Consider this to be a ritual and create a sacred space accordingly.

Clean and organize the room. Remove any clutter. Place some fresh flowers in the room. Heat or cool the room to a pleasant temperature. Make sure you will not be disturbed and switch off your phone and other devices.

Music, scent, taste and touch sensations such as silk bed sheets or lingerie can arouse you nearly as well as a good lover. Put a sarong or large piece of cloth on the bed. Have some pillows and cushions ready for support. Light some incense and candles. Put on some sensual music. Anything that feels sexy, feminine or arousing for you is perfect.

The main idea is to create the kind of space that feels special and sacred to you. You don't have to do all of these things every time, but consider trying this for your first conscious self-love practice and from time to time as you feel inspired to.

Touch your whole body

Your whole body is sensitive, pleasurable, erogenous and orgasmic. It's true that some areas of your body – such as your yoni and your breasts – are more sensitive than other parts. However, all of your body can be sensitive, pleasurable and even orgasmic if you take enough time to explore and extend your attention to other areas. The more you do, the more orgasmic you become.

I'm sure you have experienced a man touching your body too early or focusing too much on your breasts and then your vagina with the aim of getting to penetration and ejaculation. It doesn't feel very inspiring, does it? Your self-pleasure needs to include your whole body too.

So where do you touch? Everywhere! Whole-body arousal is what leads to whole-body orgasm. Although it's good to focus on one area or one kind of touch, it's also important to bring touch, sensation and pleasure to your entire body. For example, you can explore internal stimulation with one hand and use your other hand to caress, knead, pinch and touch the rest of your body. Allowing your hips to move and undulate also helps to engage your whole body. The more areas you arouse in your body, the more pleasure you will experience.

It's true that there are women who prefer intense or genital-focused touch without much of a warm-up. Some women can get aroused with hardly any foreplay, love-play, whole-body touch or preparation. But even these women can enjoy and appreciate a more gradual approach and whole-body touch every once in a while as a part of their range.

Also remember to touch your own body – all of it – throughout the day, when you make love and specifically when you self-pleasure. Explore new ways of touching your body.

Use steady stimulation

Pleasure and orgasm come from steady and consistent stimulation of the same area. One of the reasons that women experience clitoral orgasms (apart from the ultra sensitivity of the clitoris) is that they focus on one spot for a given length of time. One of the reasons women have difficulty experiencing non-clitoral orgasms is that they don't build their pleasure long enough in one place. I've often noticed women begin to experience some pleasure in a part of their body and then suddenly change what they were doing. Maybe they touch another place or move in a different way. The pleasure they were just experiencing decreases and has to be built all over again.

This can happen when you receive touch as well. Assuming your partner touches you in a way that facilitates deep and meaningful pleasure, encourage your lover to focus on one kind of touch for at least a few minutes at a time so that your pleasure has time to build. The same goes for self-pleasure – experiment with different techniques and all kinds of touch for long enough to see if it leads to pleasure. Then when it does, keep doing that for as long as you can. In time, you will develop an intuition for when to focus on one place or technique and when to change frequently in natural flow.

Accumulate your pleasure and embrace the intensity

Your orgasm is an experience of pleasure and energy. The more pleasure you generate and accumulate, the stronger and longer your orgasmic state will be. This is why explosive clitoral orgasms are not serving you– you lose some of your built-up sexual energy. It's also why it's good to build the pleasure and energy in one area for a while.

Most women and men release their sexual energy because they don't know how to handle it. It might feel like it's 'too much.' But allowing yourself to accumulate and contain this intense energy will cause you to experience stronger orgasms with less effort. Accumulating your sexual energy will also help you accumulate and contain energy in your daily life – creative energy, leadership energy, financial energy and spiritual energy.

Orgasm is the accumulation of pleasure, not the release of pleasure.

Learn how to embrace and contain the intensity of your experience. You can explore this intensity with your breath, sounds, movements and touch. The stronger, faster and deeper you are able to breathe, make sounds, move and touch yourself – the stronger, deeper and longer your orgasms can be. Try to relax into the intensity without needing to understand it or control it.

Step into the unknown

Many women stop themselves on the verge of orgasm because they feel they are about to lose control. As if they are about to face something they can't handle or something unknown. They may fear that they won't be able to handle the intensity of the pleasure, sensations, energy or emotions. Or they might feel that they are about to faint or lose consciousness. In a personal example, my lover lost control over her body during sex once. And then she couldn't see anything. She felt like she was choking and thought she was going to die. But after a few moments, she had a huge emotional release and the intensity passed. She didn't experience this phenomenon anymore and, instead, was able to experience more sexual pleasure.

When you start your orgasmic explorations, you may experience some weird bodily reactions. For example, your hands may feel charged with energy and electricity or as though you have pins and needles or they might become numb. Sometimes, it can become difficult to control your hands and they might lock in a kind of crab-claw gesture, with your thumb 'stuck' to your middle and index fingers. Your arm muscles might also tense and lock causing your elbow joint to close, with the palms close to the shoulders. A friend of mine that has experienced this calls it the 'T-Rex.' This condition is actually called 'Tetni' and it is caused by energy moving through your body and hitting resistance or blockages.

When your body is overwhelmed with energy, it tenses up. Tetni is also related to energy rising to the level of your heart chakra, and some consider it an expression of Kundalini energy. You may experience your mouth and face going numb or tingling. And in extreme cases, your whole body might become numb or you might feel extremely disorientated and like you're about to faint.

The important thing to do, as always, is to relax. Don't try to resist, fight or understand these symptoms. Simply allow your hands to go numb or lock or whatever phenomenon you are experiencing. Keep breathing and making sounds and just allow your body to move as it wants to. I assure you that once you relax, these conditions will pass and as you continue on your sexual journey, you will likely experience less and less of them.

It's okay to feel some fear, anxiety or confusion about what's happening to you and about what might happen if you step beyond a certain threshold. What's beyond that threshold might be emotions or memories that you have suppressed for years. Going there might bring on a strong emotional release or an orgasm that transports you beyond yourself. So I invite you to accept and embrace any fear you might feel and allow yourself to step into that unknown place.

Feel the fear and do it anyway.

Understand that orgasm can come in moments of grief as well as in moments of elation. It's natural to think about orgasm as something related to joy, happiness and relaxation. However, for some women, orgasm comes in times of deep grief, suffering and challenge. I know a woman who liked and enjoyed sex, but never experienced orgasm until her sister was on her deathbed. She had sex that night in a state of total grief, knowing that her beloved sister was about to die. And she experienced her first orgasm that night. The grief and frustration somehow helped her to surrender and let go. The intensity of the feelings she allowed herself to embrace turned into orgasm.

Remember that emotion is energy. And any strong emotion can be transformed into orgasm.

It's time to practice

Knowledge might be power, but you're not here just to *read* about orgasms, are you? You need to put the information into practice if you intend to increase your orgasmic power.

The practices I share with you are like building blocks that you can use by yourself, with your current or future partner and even in non-sexual situations. They will have a profound effect on your health and wellbeing, not to mention the depth of your orgasmic ability.

Remember, female arousal takes time to build into orgasm, so stay present with the pleasure. Also be aware that you might need to find the right touch at the right place at the right time.

Embodiment practice – Self-pleasuring ritual

Whether you masturbate regularly or not, try to regard this practice as a self-pleasuring ritual.

Self-reflection: *How do you usually pleasure yourself? What do you do to intensify your pleasure?*

Here are a few things you can try when you touch yourself:

- Relax and let go – one of the most powerful attitudes for your orgasmic experience.
- Build intensity gradually – from light touch to strong touch.
- Gradually deepen your touch – from the surface of your skin to grabbing flesh and feeling your bones underneath the flesh.
- Move from the outside in – from the edges of the body (your hands, head and feet) across your body (your thighs, chest and belly) and finally toward your center (your yoni).
- From external to internal – from the external surfaces of your yoni to the depths internally.

I recommend dedicating at least one hour when you are alone and won't be interrupted. If you share a house with other people and are self-conscious, you can try to find a time when they are out. I recommend not using a vibrator because these create unnatural stimulation that no human being can create. Also, be sure to switch off all of your gadgets – phone, iPad, laptop, and so on.

When you are ready, begin your ritual:

1. Set up a 'love nest' in your bedroom. Prepare the space as we discussed previously in a way that feels special or sacred to you.
2. Prepare yourself for your pleasure. Take a long, hot bath or at least a nice, long shower. You might like to use scented oils or salts.
3. Lie on your bed and smear yourself with some good massage oil. I recommend coconut, almond, avocado, grape-seed or another quality oil. It should be cold-pressed and edible since your body will absorb the oil through your skin.

4. Start touching yourself. Bring awareness, touch and sensation to your entire body. Focus on your thighs, buttocks, belly, chest, breasts, hands, arms, neck and scalp before you touch your yoni. It's important to activate your entire body so your sexual energy doesn't stay confined to your genital area.

5. Build your arousal and pleasure gradually. If you aren't feeling aroused, continue to caress your body and massage your yoni. Focus on the sensations. Be aware of any small wave of pleasure. Make sure you breathe fully in and out of your belly. Explore making sounds. Explore moving your hips back and forth and side to side.

6. Make sure you don't just focus on your clit. Try not to have a clitoral orgasm, as that might deplete your energy and cause you to stop wanting more pleasure.

7. When you feel ready, start experimenting with internal stimulation using your fingers, a dildo or a penis-shaped vegetable. Aim for this to be the majority of your self-pleasuring experience.

8. It's okay if you experience feelings of fear, anxiety or resistance coming up. These might be emotions and memories that have been suppressed for years. Or it could be the fear of letting go and surrendering into an orgasm deeper than any you have ever experienced. Either keep going or pause to witness your fear. Allow yourself to experience and express it. Then, keep going. Celebrate and enjoy whatever sensations or emotions come up.

9. Relax into your orgasm if it comes – enjoy it and keep going. If it doesn't, accept the pleasure you did experience as an orgasmic state. The goal isn't to have an orgasm but to connect with yourself. Have an attitude of curiosity, exploration and discovery.

If you can create a self-pleasuring ritual for yourself as a daily practice, you will notice your body opening and becoming more sensitive, pleasurable and orgasmic. Consider making a commitment to self-pleasure every single day (or at least three times a week) for *at least* twenty minutes over the next month. Try to make time for an hour-long session once a week.

Even when you are in a relationship, it's so important to keep having frequent sex with the most important person in your life – *you.* It's not meant to replace the natural human connection that we deeply yearn for with another person – on the sexual, emotional, mental and spiritual levels. However, you need to build this connection with yourself in order to experience it fully with others, and one way to do that is by having sex with yourself in the same way that you would like your partner to have sex with you.

The self-pleasure tapas

When you commit to do something every day, that thing is given importance and meaning. Daily self-pleasure is one of the most important practices that I guide my clients to embrace. Many women who have set aside enough time for this and have completed this self-pleasure challenge have experienced huge shifts and transformations in their sexuality, their orgasmic experience, their self-confidence and their feelings of femininity.

The Tantrics call a daily practice like this 'tapas' and include it as one of the ten spiritual precepts known as the Yamas and Niyamas. These are kind of like the ten commandments of yoga. Some people translate tapas as 'austerity' but it actually means commitment or determination. Taking a tapas means you make a commitment to do a particular kind of spiritual practice for a certain time period. For example, meditating for half an hour every morning, practicing yoga every day, giving money to charity or avoiding particular foods, like meat. Taking a tapas is the ancient way of creating new and empowering habits.

You can take a tapas for any length of time, but thirty days is considered the minimum length you need to feel the effects of your practice and to adopt the new habit. So, I invite you to take a thirty-day tapas.

Will you make a commitment to practice self-pleasure for at least twenty minutes every day for one month? Let twenty minutes be your minimum. The reason I've set it this low is so you will still be able to do it even on days when you're busy, tired, stressed or not in the mood. Where possible, it is far more powerful to aim for thirty to forty-five minutes.

Does this sound like too much? Think of it like this: If you had an amazing lover who made you feel fully orgasmic, would you have sex with him every day for half an hour? I think you might be inspired to! So I invite you to discover your own inner lover and make love with her every day for the same reason.

During your tapas, you can enjoy clitoral stimulation, but it's crucial that you avoid clitoral orgasms. You want to avoid losing your sexual energy and also experiencing that quick release. Instead, let your tapas be about honoring and connecting to your body and yourself. Even if you already experience internal peak orgasms, such as a G-spot orgasm, I suggest during this month you use the 'edging' technique to stop before any kind of orgasmic peak. You will notice that when you do this, your whole day will become orgasmic. And I don't mean this in a poetic way. You will actually experience pleasure sensations throughout your day.

Your practice should be a self-pleasure ritual as we have previously discussed. Avoid mechanical motions and, instead, create a practice of exploring, loving and connecting to your yoni, your sexuality and your femininity. It's important that you try to include internal stimulation because there is meaning and importance behind this during your tapas (we'll look at the importance of this soon).

And if you aren't ready for internal stimulation on a particular day, then pleasure yourself externally. If you don't even feel like doing that, that's okay too. Use your practice time to simply put one hand on your yoni and another hand on your breast or heart chakra. Be gentle with yourself.

After a few days or weeks of practice, you might start to experience new kinds of pleasure and orgasm. Enjoy them but don't get attached to them. You might orgasm every day for a week and then experience pain and emotion that you've suppressed for years the following week. Embrace whatever is coming up and keep going. This is a process.

Do this practice even if you have a regular sex life and on the days when you menstruate. There might be days when you feel totally disconnected, frigid, switched off, distant or depressed. You might have resistance or very strong emotions coming up. Allow yourself to express the emotions verbally with words and sounds, and physically with movement.

If you don't do your practice on a particular day, don't use it as an excuse to stop your thirty-day commitment. Just keep going the next day and add two days at the end of the one-month period. One day to make up for the day that you've missed and one day as a prize for your persistence.

Use this practice as an act of self-love and self-connection. The idea is to learn how to connect with yourself, arouse yourself, pleasure yourself and satisfy yourself *by yourself*, without being dependent on a partner.

Write down your experiences in your orgasmic diary every day, even if they seem meaningless or superficial. At the end of the month, you will be able to clearly see your progress.

Completing a self-pleasure tapas will embody your commitment to yourself, your pleasure and your orgasmic power. It's an effective way to increase your pleasure and your orgasmic range very quickly.

I have guided many women on their orgasmic journeys. Those who have practiced a self-pleasuring ritual every day for a month have seen huge shifts and transformations. And not just in their orgasmic experiences – also in how feminine they feel, how orgasmic they feel throughout the day and how confident they feel with others. This daily practice is probably *the most important* in this book.

I invite you to make this commitment to yourself and witness your life change! Self-pleasure is a form of self-love and to be fully orgasmic you need to love yourself, your sexuality and, obviously, your feminine body.

The breast connection

Breasts have the power to feed a baby for the first few months of his or her life. They are the first experience many people have of love and nurture. But a woman's breasts are obviously also important to her own femininity, sexuality and orgasmic empowerment.

Self-reflection: *How connected to your breasts do you feel? Do you love them? How much pleasure can you feel when you touch them?*

As a woman, arousal ignites in your upper body and travels to your lower body. When you arouse your nipples and breasts, the orgasmic energy opens and arouses your yoni. The more sensitive and receptive your breasts are – the easier you can get aroused and the more orgasmic you can become.

Your breasts aren't simply a receptive erogenous zone, though. Your chest, heart and – to some extent – your breasts are your positive emissive center. This is in the same way that a man's cock is his positive emissive center. This is the basis of masculine-feminine polarity. A woman's positive (or emissive) pole is where a man's negative (or receptive) pole is. And vice versa. A man wants to give, to express, to emit from his cock while a woman yearns to give and emit from her heart. This may be by giving love or even via breastfeeding, which is a physical gift of life-sustaining nourishment from your breasts.

Regarding the receptive centers, a man enjoys receiving into his heart and a woman enjoys and even yearns to receive into her yoni.

The connection you have with your breasts can affect your masculine-feminine polarity as well as your orgasmic ability. I've seen women with tiny breasts, huge breasts, disproportionate breasts or saggy breasts who totally loved their breasts and had a good connection with them. This connection made them feel attractive and, therefore, they *were* attractive, to men in particular.

Small-breasted women can be naturally more sensitive than large breasted women and I often call this 'the revenge of the small-breasted women.' It's a good compensation for having smaller breasts than their bustier girlfriends. However, when a woman starts connecting to her breasts, she becomes much more sensitive and orgasmic in her breasts regardless of their size.

I was with a lover who breast-fed her three babies for eight years, one after the other. She was in her late thirties when we were together and her breasts were already sagging and smaller than they'd ever been since puberty. But she loved her body and her breasts. She experienced pleasure and intense orgasm just from her breasts and nipples being touched, kissed, licked, sucked or twisted. And I loved her breasts because she loved them. They were so sensitive, so responsive, so orgasmic. Her breasts were fully alive; they would 'sing' in my hands. They felt like an active emissive source of energy, nurturing and love.

Are we for or against bras?

As much as I love women and breasts, I'm no expert in breasts or bras so please take the following ideas on board in that light and simply see if they feel right for you.

It has become fairly common knowledge that bras restrict the natural flow of blood in a woman's breasts and can prevent the drainage of lymph nodes in this area. But bras have an energetic effect as well – they restrict the heart chakra and various energy points around the chest. Yet another argument against bras is that breasts may be more prone to sagging because bras prevent the growth of supporting breast tissue and contribute to them losing their natural muscle strength. In other words, wearing a bra doesn't necessarily prevent sagging as is often claimed, and might actually cause sagging! There is even anecdotal evidence that wearing a bra is connected to breast cancer, although this has not been scientifically proven.

Additionally, women with small breasts often don't need to wear a bra. Many will do so to conform to a social standard or to prevent their nipples from showing. However, if this bothers you, you could always consider wearing a camisole or tank top under your outer clothes. If you have small breasts, you can choose to love and adore your breasts as symbols of youthful femininity. You can rejoice that you don't need to wear a bra and that your breasts don't interfere with jogging or exercising. And they will sag very little, if at all. Contrary to common beliefs and social conditioning, many men actually love and prefer women with small breasts.

On the other hand, women with large breasts often feel they need a bra for comfort and support. That is understandable. However, there are specific muscle exercises that can make your breasts a bit smaller or support their structure, which means even women with larger breasts can avoid the blood-flow and energy restriction that comes from wearing bras if they choose to give up the bra for at least some of the day. Consulting with a professional fitness trainer is recommended.

If you have large breasts, you can choose to love and adore your breasts as symbols of abundant femininity and embrace the attention you get. The reaction of men (and women!) to large breasts is an automatic evolutionary one, related to our perception of fertility and childbearing ability (as well as a few unresolved mummy issues).

If you do choose to wear a bra, try to avoid bras with a metal underwire as these have the worst effect on your body, both physically and energetically. Also, be aware that many women don't wear the right kind or size of bra for their breasts. Consider going to a shop that offers a proper bra fitting service. Have your measurements taken and find a bra that really fits you. And one that makes you feel feminine and connected to your breasts!

Orgasmic extras

For more information on this topic, you can check out this article: www.collective-evolution.com/2014/04/16/ladies-its-finally-time-to-take-off-that-bra-for-good

You can also Google 'underwire bras side effects.'

What about breast implants?

It's important that you learn to love your breasts as they are, regardless of their shape and size. So I generally advise against getting breast implants. There are many side effects to be aware of if you have them or are considering getting them. For example, implants can rupture and the contents can seep out into your body. Also, although many women are happy with their implants, I have perceived a kind of emotional and energetic disconnection between some of these women and their breasts.

Fortunately, there has been a body-positive shift in the media recently. Hollywood is beginning to celebrate small-breasted actresses such as Keira Knightley, Rachel McAdams and Natalie Portman. It seems that breast implants are finally going out of fashion.

However, if you really want larger breasts, it's actually possible to grow them naturally. You can do this with a combination of massage, intention, visualization, diet, exercise and a ton of specific yogic techniques. I'm talking about one to two hours per day for a period spanning a few months to a year. Personally, I'd say that your effort is better directed at other things, but if you're really keen to do this, I can guide you as a private client.

And if you already have breast implants, you can still develop your breast connection with the practices included in this topic.

Why the breast connection matters

The main point to remember is that your connection to your breasts is important. They need to be loved and accepted as a part of your womanly self, just like your vagina.

Touching your breasts can support your connection to them. And frequent breast massage is beneficial as it:

- Connects you to your femininity, body and sexuality.
- Improves the blood flow in, lymphatic drainage from and energy flow to your breasts, making them healthier and potentially reducing the risk of cysts or tumors.
- Can heal past trauma around your breasts, body and sexuality.
- Helps to move stagnant energy out of your breasts.
- Activates your heart chakra.
- Arouses you sexually.
- Improves your body image and self-acceptance.
- Can help your breasts become suppler and possibly even slightly bigger when combined with other practices.

Perhaps you judge your breasts too small, too big, too uneven or not quite right. If so, it's time to love and accept them. Maybe you'd like to feel deeper pleasure when you or your lover touches your breasts. Well, connecting to your breasts will help with this. Let's explore some practices that support your breast connection.

Embodiment practice – Connecting with your breasts

Simply looking at yourself in the mirror and actively loving and worshipping your breasts is a way to connect with them. However, this practice focuses on touch.

1. Lie down naked and hold your breasts in your hands. Do this in whatever way feels right for you.
2. Close your eyes and just feel them. What are your breasts feeling? What are they saying? What kind of touch do they want from you and your partner? How do they want to be loved?
3. Talk to your breasts. Ask them for forgiveness if you haven't loved them and treated them well. Affirm that you love them and tell them what you love about them.
4. Accept and express whatever emotions come up in this practice with words, sounds or movements.
5. Continue this for ten to fifteen minutes and then write down your experience in your orgasmic diary.

This simple practice is the first step in connecting to your breasts. When you have opened the connection, you can deepen this further with massage.

Embodiment practice – Breast massage

Frequent breast massage has many benefits and can create a deeper connection between you and your breasts. This practice offers one way you can do this.

Note: Women who have cysts or tumors in their breasts should seek advice from complementary medicine professionals before practicing breast massage.

1. Start by cupping your breasts with both of your hands and connecting with them, similar to the previous practice.
2. Then, while cupping your breasts, push or lift them very slightly upwards towards your shoulders. Hold them there for a couple of minutes. This facilitates feelings of connection, nurturing, acceptance and support. If possible, hold them slightly from underneath so your hand touches your chest along the bra line, but don't worry if this is not possible or convenient for you.
3. Start moving your hands, palms, wrists and forearms across the skin of your breasts. Use a light to medium touch, relating to the air and water elements we covered in the touch practices earlier. This activates your skin without going deep into the tissue of your breasts.
4. Wait a few minutes before starting to touch your nipples. Then, as you start touching your nipples, remember to involve them but don't make them the center of your attention. Continue for three to ten minutes.
5. Next, start massaging the tissue of your breasts. Knead them with your palms and fingers, push the heel of your hand into your flesh and squeeze your flesh between two or more fingers. Make sure that you are moving your breast tissue in all directions – up, down, left and right – as well as pushing into your body and pulling outwards.

6. Also consider bouncing your breasts up and down, from side to side and bouncing them against each other if that doesn't hurt. You can do this one breast at a time using both hands or simultaneously with both of your breasts at the same time.

7. Massage without oil first, to make use of the friction of your skin. Then apply good-quality oil and continue massaging your breasts. Aim to spend at least ten minutes on this part of your massage.

8. Massage both breasts together and then use both hands to massage each of your breasts individually.

9. When you're finished, relax and note the sensations, emotions and insights you received from this practice, and write them down in your orgasmic diary.

Aim to give yourself a breast massage two to four times per week while you are actively exploring your orgasmic journey, and especially if you feel disconnected from your breasts. Going forward, I still recommend doing this at least once a week. You can do this practice on its own or combine it with self-pleasuring. You will notice that your breasts become more and more sensitive and that your pleasure expands.

The other part of your feminine body that calls for love and connection is, of course, your vagina.

Love your vagina

Vaginal love, awareness, health, pleasure and appreciation are all connected to your orgasmic power. Many women I work with don't have a good connection with this part of their body, which is so important to their femininity. Even while they might look feminine, without this connection they don't *feel* deeply feminine, juicy or sexual. Or they might only express a small range of feminine energies. But the women who do have a strong connection with their vagina experience greater awareness and control of their sexuality, and are usually more orgasmic, feminine and sexually expressive.

Self-reflection: *How connected do you feel with your vagina?*

Your connection with your vagina is your connection with your femininity. It is related to your expression as a woman and to some extent your life force. This then influences your relationships with the women in your life – your mother, sisters, daughters and female friends – and also affects the sort of men you attract. And this is regardless of the kind of interaction you may have with them, be it sexual, romantic, friendly, social or professional.

Your connection with your vagina and your femininity also affects you personally – your intuition, your creativity and your spiritual practice. It can make you either rigid or flexible, whether that is in your body, thoughts or actions. And, obviously, your connection with your vagina determines how orgasmic, sexually expressive and sensual you are.

Perhaps you're thinking, 'I don't feel that connected to my vagina but I'm creative and successful anyway!' Well, that's great. Now, imagine what could be possible if you were fully and deeply connected to your vagina, your yoni, your pussy. What if it enabled you to be even more creative and successful? What if this effect flowed into other areas of your life?

Becoming more connected to your vagina means you acknowledge her power, admire her beauty, love her juiciness and give her the gift of healing when she needs it.

Acknowledge her

Some women refer to their vagina as 'it,' which can create distance and separation from this intimate part of yourself. To avoid this kind of disconnect, I recommend you refer to your vagina as 'she.'

Your vagina is a 'She.'

So with this in mind, what is her name? Is it 'vagina'? Vagina. Vagina. Vagina. How does that feel for you? By the way, vagina refers to the internal vaginal tube, while the correct name for the outer area and lips is 'vulva.' But for the sake of simplicity, I'm using the word 'vagina' to refer to both your vulva and vaginal passage.

The words we use, the sound of words and the cultural baggage around words greatly affects our perception and experience of what the words refer to. Think about some other names and words that you could use instead of vagina. You might notice that some are endearing, some are neutral and others feel condescending or even abusive.

I love languages and get excited by the sound of some words. Personally, 'vagina' isn't my favorite name for her. To me, it sounds harsh and angular, a bit mechanical and slightly cold. I prefer to use 'yoni' (pronounced yo-nee), which is a Sanskrit word – the ancient language of India. I love how 'yoni' sounds. To me, it sounds warm, soft, vibrating, sensual and open. 'Yowww-neeeee … Yiiiiiowneeee … Yiiiiiooooooooow-nnnnnneeee…'

Yoni – Sacred flower, temple, space or passage.

'Pussy' is another important word used to describe female genitalia. Many people have negative associations with this word and some use it as a derogatory word, for example, 'Don't be a pussy.' But pussy can also be a powerful word, deeply connected with the rawness, wildness, juiciness and power of your ... well ... pussy. If you shy away from this word, ask yourself if you also shy away from these aspects of your sexuality and your life. Would you ask your lover to kiss your vagina or to kiss your pussy?

Use whatever word feels good for you; just make sure you're not avoiding anything.

Perhaps you would like to experiment referring to your vagina as 'yoni' or another positive or endearing name. By all means, if you love the sound of 'vagina,' or any other word you use, please continue to use it – she is a part of your body and should be named lovingly by you.

I will use both yoni and vagina, so please read these as your own favorite name if it is different to what I use.

Now that we've addressed how you acknowledge your vagina, take a moment to think about what your relationship with her is like.

Embodiment practice – Getting to know your vagina

Before you can truly love and appreciate your vagina, you need to get to know her. And that often begins with taking a look at how you feel about her.

1. How do you feel about her?

   First of all, divide a page of your diary into two sections and then write down all of the positive sensations, thoughts, judgments, feelings, perceptions and experiences related to your vagina on one side. For example, 'I love how my pussy pulsates when I'm aroused' or 'I love how she changes throughout the month.'

Then do the same on the other side for all of the negative associations as well. For example, 'I don't like my hairy pussy' or 'I get yeast infections often and I hate it' or 'My partner penetrated me before I was ready and my vagina hurt after sex.'

Write these associations down without censoring them or trying to understand them. Aim to write down at least twenty to thirty associations in total. More is better. After writing down your associations with your own vagina, write down a few more words that relate to your perception of vaginas in general.

Once you have finished, reflect on your list and ask yourself whether your perception of your vagina is mostly positive or negative. How could this be affecting your relationships, motherhood, friendships, joy, creativity, career and state of being? Consider describing this in your diary. The more you are aware of how your perceptions and tendencies are affecting you – the more you are motivated to change those that are not serving you.

2. Clear any limiting beliefs

It's worthwhile taking a closer look at the negative associations you wrote down and clearing any that might be limiting your experience of your femininity, your sexuality and your orgasmic experience. For each of your negative beliefs, ask yourself:

- Is it true? Are you absolutely sure that it's true?
- What if the opposite of this limiting belief was true? How would that feel? How would different aspects of your life be affected?
- What actions could you take to help you let go of this limiting belief? What could you do to embrace an empowering belief instead?

These questions are inspired by Byron Katie's *The Work* and are a powerful way of releasing beliefs that don't serve you. If you need my help in dissolving your limiting beliefs to become more connected with your femininity, orgasm and confidence, check out the online resources section of my website for details about my coaching service (www.intimatepower.com/orgasm-book-resources). The following steps will also help to dissolve the effects of any limiting beliefs about your vagina.

3. Feel your vagina

While it's empowering to form positive and loving associations with you vagina, it is equally important to be present to how she feels in any given moment. After reading the following questions, close your eyes and become fully aware of your vagina:

- How well can you feel her?
- Is she warm or cold?
- Is she dry, moist or dripping wet?
- Is she contracted and tense or expanded and relaxed?
- Is she aroused or shut down?
- Is she throbbing or pulsating?
- How deep inside her can you perceive?
- Is she happy or sad?
- How connected to her do you feel?
- Do you love her?

After feeling into her for a few minutes, take some time to write down your responses in your orgasmic diary. Consider doing this practice every morning or as preparation for your self-pleasuring practice. You can also feel into her throughout the day. The more you are able to feel your vagina, the more you will feel *within* your vagina and your whole body. You may even feel like you have acquired an entirely new erogenous zone, almost like another clitoris but bigger and much more pleasurable.

The more you feel your yoni – the more your yoni will feel.

---

4. Let her speak

   Imagine if your vagina could speak. What would she say? When you listen to your vagina, you become better connected with her and better able to love and honor her. You don't need to understand her; she doesn't need to make sense. Just *let her speak*!

   She should be allowed to speak in the first person. For example, 'I am a bit cold right now and I would like you to touch me more often' or 'I don't want you to allow anyone inside me if I'm not ready' or 'I would love you to use a big dildo to explore all of me.'

   So, what does your vagina have to say?

   - How does she describe herself?
   - How is she feeling right now?
   - What does she want to tell you?
   - Is she angry about anything?
   - What does she love?
   - What does she want from you?
   - What does she want from your partner?

Write down what your vagina tells you in your orgasmic diary.

You will be able to better respect, serve and satisfy your vagina when you listen to what she has to say. What can you do for her right now? What can you do for her on a regular basis? Is there anything you need to stop doing? Make a commitment to love her the way she wants to be loved.

Getting to know your vagina is a powerful practice that you might consider revisiting every month or whenever you feel disconnected from your vagina. This is a critical step towards loving her. And loving her is deeply connected to your sexuality and femininity.

Look at her

It's important to know and love the sight of your yoni. This affects your personal connection with her and also the level of comfort you feel when a man is looking at you – and at her. If you don't love the sight of your yoni, it will become a limitation or an inhibition of your sexuality.

Self-reflection: *How do you feel about the shape and size of your vagina?*

Think about your yoni for a moment. How often do you look at her? Do you like what you see? Do you ever feel self-conscious or embarrassed about how she looks? Do you think your yoni is different, unattractive or inferior to other women's yonis that you've seen in either real-life or porn?

Many women feel that their vaginas are unattractive compared to what they see in the media, namely in porn. The porn industry has created a kind of standard for how vaginas should look – a shaved pussy with the inner lips tucked in and not protruding. In fact, some countries have laws that demand pubic hair be digitally removed in soft porn images, effectively rendering the infantile vagina of a young girl the norm.

These 'standards' have led to the rise of labiaplasty, which is genital cosmetic surgery that literally cuts a woman's labia to replicate the porn industry standard. This unnatural standard of vagina is known as a 'designer vagina.' Instead of accepting themselves and their body as they are, women that go under the knife end up mutilating a sacred, beautiful and sensitive part of their body, all in the name of an imposed and unnatural beauty standard. This creates further disconnection between the woman and her feminine core. The medical procedure also creates a kind of trauma in the body, and that woman might even lose some of her pleasure and orgasmic capacity owing to the severing of nerves in the area.

The truth is that women's vaginas come in all shapes and sizes. The inner lips can be tiny or they can protrude well outside of the yoni. The clitoris might be as big as a pea, visible and protruding. Or it can be much smaller and completely hidden under the clitoral hood. Most labia are asymmetric, either slightly or significantly, with one lip larger than the other. The color of labia ranges from light pink to dark brown and is often not uniform in color. And, obviously, all women have different pubic hair, some sparse and others dense, covering the whole triangle area of the crotch and extending to the upper thighs.

So whatever your yoni looks like – she is normal and beautiful. There is no standard she should be expected to adhere to. You will deepen your connection with her if you love how she looks. So let's work on that – it's time for some yoni gazing! *(see Diagram 3 on page 85)*

Labia

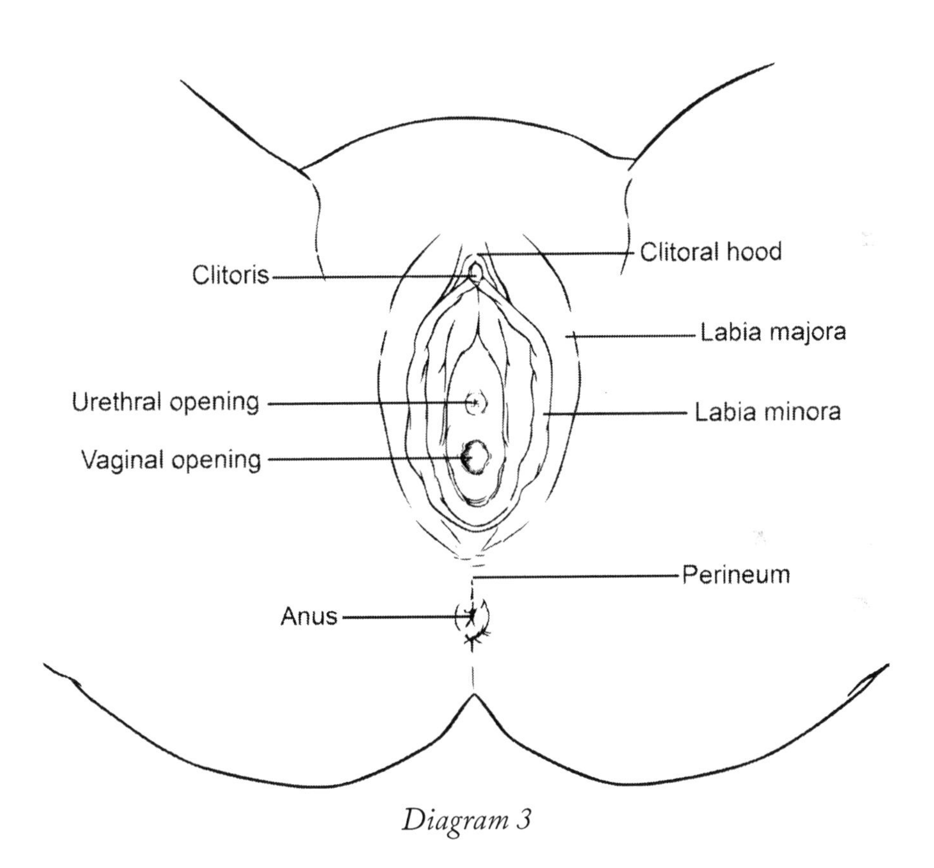

Diagram 3

Orgasmic extras

101 Vagina – www.101vagina.com

Photographer and activist Philip Werner has created an exhibition and coffee table book that celebrates the variety of vulvas out there. Each pictured woman also shares a few words about her experience with her vagina.

The heart of the flower – www.onelove.net.au/the-book

Sexual educators Andrew Barnes and Yvonne Lumsden have created a book of exquisite photos of vulvas. It also includes some anatomy info.

Embodiment practice – Gazing at your yoni

This practice is about looking at your yoni and accepting what you see. If you can accept her, you can love her. And if you love her, you can fully experience her and her orgasmic power.

Try to find a small mirror that stands by itself or one that you can hold in your hand or lean against a book; just make sure it doesn't have sharp edges. You could also crouch over a mirror on the floor, although you probably wouldn't want to do this for too long.

1. Start by standing naked and looking at your body in front of a large mirror. Then look specifically at your yoni. Look at her as if it's the first time you've seen her or any other yoni.

2. Next, sit on the floor with your legs spread and your back against the wall. Place your small mirror in front of your yoni. Look at her.
3. Start touching your yoni and see how she looks inside. Part your lips with your fingers and notice what your labia look like. Notice your clitoris and the clitoral hood. See you outer and inner lips and how they connect with the rest of your yoni.
4. When you are looking at your yoni, first do so in a passive way. Simply observe, notice, witness and explore what she looks like. Try not to judge or criticize what you see.
5. Then, look at your yoni in an active way. Actively love and appreciate what you see.

Another thing you can try is using the video function on your smartphone, with the front-facing camera. You can either watch the screen or you can make a video of your yoni. Now that's technology in the service of sexual liberation!

Gazing at your yoni will help you love and accept how she looks, which will also help you to feel more comfortable when a lover is looking at you or going down on you.

Orgasmic extras

This exercise was partly inspired by an American sexual educator called Betti Dodson. She is known for helping women connect with the sight of their yonis, among other things. Check her stuff out at www.dodsonandross.com

Next-level yoni gazing

Loving the sight of your yoni is already very empowering but there is a 'next level' practice for those who want to explore the orgasmic power of their yonis further.

If you feel ready, continue on from the previous practice. While you are looking at your yoni, start to pleasure yourself. Begin with your fingers and then try a dildo or a similar object.

Notice how your yoni changes shape and color. See how your lips engorge and your yoni physically opens to receive your touch. Observe the dildo going into your yoni; see how she 'swallows' it. Notice how juicy she is. Make sure that you're not simply masturbating for a quick release during this practice. Make love with your yoni and look her 'in the eyes' while doing so.

This practice will supercharge your connection with your beautiful and orgasmic yoni.

Love your juiciness

As a sexual coach, I often encourage a woman to smear her fingers in her vaginal juices and bring them up to her nose and mouth. Some women turn their face away in disgust at this suggestion. And, almost without fail, these are the women who are less connected to their femininity, less sexual and less orgasmic than they would like to be. Which is why some of them sought my guidance in the first place.

Self-reflection: *Do you have any resistance to smelling or tasting your vaginal juices?*

If you don't appreciate the smell or taste of your yoni, how can you expect your partner to like them? It's crucial that you learn to love your yoni in this way.

It's true that some women experience unpleasant smells or tastes in their vaginas from time to time, often owing to a pH imbalance, fungal growth or an STI. If you detect a smell or taste that is very unpleasant, I suggest a check-up with your doctor to make sure you don't have any of these conditions. If you do have a health issue, you can address this and bring your vagina back to good health, whereby she has her own unique and healthy smell and taste. Also, I suggest trying natural remedies in the first instance.

Being able to appreciate your juiciness is an important aspect of your journey to better connect with your vagina, body, femininity, sexuality, pleasure and orgasm. It's as though your yoni is a person and you're learning to get to know her and love more aspects of her. Also, most men get excited to see a woman tasting herself. Smearing your fingers with your juices and offering them to your lover to smell and taste is a meaningful and symbolic action. If this idea challenges you, I suggest that it might be a good idea for you to explore this further.

It's important to love and celebrate all aspects of your body, your femininity and your sexuality. When you can love your juices and juiciness, you will connect with your yoni on a deeper level.

Embodiment practice – Love your juices

Perhaps you already enjoy the different smells and tastes of your yoni. Or maybe appreciating that aspect of her is completely new to you. Either way, bringing an increased awareness and appreciation to your juices is empowering.

1. Gently insert a finger into your yoni and then bring your finger up to your nose. Smell her. What is your response? If you have any negative reaction to your smell, write it down or express it with your voice or movements.

2. Then smell your juices again. Witness your reaction and identify the 'story' around your smell. Stay with it this time without reacting or going into the story. Ask yourself, 'What do I love about my smell?' and 'How can I love and embrace my smell?'

3. Now do the same thing but taste your vaginal juices instead of smelling them. Note your reactions. Then identify what you love about your taste.

If you want to expand on this practice, you can also smell and taste your menstrual blood. Contrary to popular belief, there are no toxins or waste materials in this blood. It's actually charged with minerals and nutrients – the very stuff of life force energy! It's what supports new life in a woman's womb in the first few weeks.

Becoming more loving and accepting of *all* of your juices further embodies your self-love and feminine potency. The more you know and love her, the more you can connect with her and your own orgasmic experience.

What if you're not very juicy?

Many women suffer from vaginal dryness and either take a long time to get lubricated or don't get wet at all. This can be caused by hormonal imbalances, energetic imbalances, diet, age, the time of month or mindset around sexuality.

There are practices that can lead to increased vaginal lubrication, such as daily internal stimulation, massaging your a-spot, using a jade egg and receiving a yoni massage. We will be covering these as we move through this book. Also, make sure you drink plenty of water and eat a balanced diet with low salt intake and high in fruits and vegetables, both raw and lightly cooked. In addition, you could consider seeing a traditional Chinese medicine practitioner (TCM) or an Ayurvedic practitioner.

As a general rule, you should aim to be wet before you engage in many of the practices in this book, in particular any internal stimulation. However, if you have difficulty getting lubricated at this stage of your orgasmic journey, use oil or lube while you practice the techniques until you naturally increase your lubrication.

> *'These practices have increased my vaginal lubrication, as well as my intuition and inner-voice. This stuff works!'*

Loving your yoni and deepening your connection with her is healing and can help with vaginal dryness. This is important for both healing and pleasure, particularly when you begin to include internal touch.

> *Orgasmic extras*
>
> You might like to check out the book *Vagina: A new biography* by Naomi Wolf. She explores how society's attitude to the female genitalia affects women's sexual experiences. I highly recommend it.

The importance of internal touch

Internal touch is a powerful healing practice for your yoni. And if you have penetrative sex with your partner, you'll want to explore your own pleasure with internal stimulation as well. When you have sex with a man, do you want him to just touch you on the outside of your vagina, or do you desire penetration, for him to be inside you? The more you can experience pleasure from internal stimulation on your own, the easier it will be with a partner.

Self-reflection: *How often do you pleasure yourself internally?*

When you masturbate, it's important to explore more than just your clit and to also stimulate yourself internally. If you are only stimulating your clit during self-pleasure or don't like the idea of inserting something into your vagina, it helps to ask why this might be and then understand what you are missing out on.

The benefits of internal stimulation during self-pleasure include the following:

- You wake up the pleasure inside of your vagina. You bring awareness and increased sensation into your vagina.
- You make it easier to experience internal orgasms (such as vaginal) and other kinds of orgasms by yourself and with another person.
- You can heal past pain and trauma with this practice.
- You can release stagnant energy from within your vagina, which otherwise might cause over-emotionality, confusion, horniness and, if left unchecked, conditions such as cysts and even diseases like cancer.
- In Chinese medicine, there is a connection between different body parts and organs. Interestingly, both the entrance to your vagina and your cervix (the deepest part of your vagina) correlate to your heart. So stimulating yourself internally can improve the flow of energy throughout your body, heal ailments and decrease the possibility of future disease.
- You become more independent and empowered with your sexuality.
- You connect to and express deeper aspects of your femininity, both in the bedroom and in your daily life.

Regular internal stimulation will help you experience internal orgasms both by yourself and with a partner.

So, if you aren't including internal stimulation as a part of your self-pleasure practice, I highly recommend the next practice.

Embodiment practice – Internal self-pleasuring

Get yourself aroused and lubricated before beginning this practice. I suggest using the ideas from the previous self-pleasuring ritual. Remember to bring attention to your whole body and then move towards your more erogenous zones. During your first session, you can take it easy and light, but in following self-pleasure sessions, explore all of the steps in this practice.

When you feel ready, begin to focus on your yoni:

1. Rub the area around the entrance to your vagina for a few minutes. If you have aroused yourself enough, you might be naturally lubricated. If possible, it's important to wait until you are naturally lubricated and your yoni feels like she wants something inside her. However, if you are not lubricated enough, use saliva or a good natural oil with no essential oils or scents to create lubrication. This will ensure that your yoni is ready for penetration and internal stimulation.
2. Start by using your fingers. Insert a finger into your yoni and pause. Notice what your finger is feeling, what your yoni is feeling and what sensations and emotions come up.
3. Then explore with two or more fingers. Try to hook your fingers towards your clit from the inside. This way you are touching the areas where your G-spot is located. Apply pressure there for a while and then start pressing or squeezing the area, using different rhythms. You can apply clitoral stimulation as well – but avoid a clitoral orgasm in this practice.
4. After a while, your fingers might get tired or you might feel that you want to have something deeper or a bit bigger inside of you. I

suggest changing to a dildo, preferably a non-vibrating one. Size does matter here, and you should get a nice long one that can reach all the way into the deepest parts of your vagina, while allowing you to hold it comfortably. If you don't own a dildo, find a nice cucumber, zucchini or thick carrot. These are safe to use in place of a dildo. For simplicity, I will refer whatever object you choose to use as a dildo.

5. Make sure that you are well-lubricated. If you are going to use a lube, choose the best one for the material of the dildo you have chosen. Use a silicon-based lube for silicon objects or a natural oil for natural objects.

6. Insert the tip of the dildo into your vagina and see how that feels. Make gentle and gradual in-and-out movements and round-and-round motions. Slowly insert more and more of the dildo into your vagina, for as long as it feels comfortable. At every stage, you can pause for a moment and focus on the sensations, feelings, emotions and thoughts that come up. You might feel self-conscious, resistant or even ashamed about doing this – acknowledge that and keep going.

7. Explore different ways to hold and move the dildo. Don't just do in-and-out movements; also move the dildo in circles inside you. Explore a range of motions from very light to very intense. Rub your vaginal walls and go as deep as you can. It's important to reach all areas of your vagina.

8. You might experience some discomfort, numbness or pain. Focus on the points or areas where you feel these sensations. Massage these areas for a few minutes if you can or as long as it is bearable, while constantly expressing the sensations and emotions with your breath, sounds and body movements. After exploring an area of discomfort or pain, move to another area. Alternate between pleasure and discomfort.

9. Keep pushing slightly beyond your comfort zone. At some spots, there might be moments when the emotion you experience feels unbearable. If you stop, these emotions will stay stuck in your body. But if you keep going, you might be able to release the emotions that have been locked and suppressed for years. It's important to allow yourself to express what's coming up, otherwise the pain and trauma will stay stuck in your body. This is what makes internal stimulation such a healing practice.

10. Keep alternating between movement and stillness. If you feel that you are on the verge of orgasm, keep going, but don't be attached to any outcome.

11. Keep going for about half an hour or longer, and then take another ten minutes or so to rest and integrate your experience. It's a great idea to write about your self-pleasuring practices in your orgasmic diary.

Self-pleasuring with internal stimulation is a powerful practice. If you have never experienced a vaginal orgasm or any kind of internal orgasm, then this is the practice that will help you to experience this. And if you have experienced these and would like to strengthen your internal orgasmic power, this practice is also for you.

The healing benefits are also profound. Internal stimulation commonly causes some pain, discomfort, resistance, fear, anxiety, anger, frustration, confusion, exhaustion and other feelings and emotions. If you experience any of these, it means your vagina is holding some kind of tension, trauma or stagnant energy. Your internal self-pleasure practice can help to heal any trauma or negative energy you are holding on to.

And let's not forget the other key benefit ... your orgasmic power will significantly increase! As your self-pleasure practices become more orgasmic and exciting, you'll be ready to expand your orgasms even more.

Heal your yoni

Healing your yoni can help you to increase your capacity to experience orgasm. You can raise your awareness and sensitivity to what you experience within your yoni. You can also heal any painful spots by connecting to whatever has been suppressed and buried there.

Self-reflection: *Do you have any sore or painful areas in your vagina?*

If you have ever given or received a massage, you will know that some muscles or areas of the body can be tight or have knots in the tissues and muscles. Massaging these areas can be painful but helps to dissolve these. Similarly, the yoni is made up of muscles and soft tissue and there are often 'knots' inside a woman's yoni. These knots can be caused by sexual abuse, medical procedures and surgeries or from being penetrated before you are ready.

Knots in the yoni might feel like painful spots or numb areas and these occur when your yoni is shocked or trying to protect herself. This causes a contraction and sometimes the contraction is so strong that it doesn't get released. But this doesn't just occur on the physical level. Your yoni is the most sensitive and receptive place in your body. It's like an energetic sponge that also collects and holds energies, memories and feelings.

Sexual pain and emotion that is stuck and not expressed over many years can turn into conditions such as pH imbalances, candida or yeast infections, STIs, urinary tract infections (UTIs), cysts and, in extreme cases, cancers. This stuff wants to come out. It wants to be released. For example, you might feel compelled to cry, shout, curse or hit the mattress with your fists. If you don't express these emotions, they will sink back into your body and your psyche and then re-surface again later.

You can heal these knots with a practice that touches all of the points inside your yoni. When a woman receives a yoni massage, emotions and memories that have been suppressed and locked in the cells for years or even decades are often expressed and released. This can also happen when you engage in conscious sex.

Yoni massage can help to heal the knots within your vagina. This practice can be a couple's exercise where another person facilitates the mapping for you and holds space while you process whatever comes up. But doing this by yourself is a great place to start and also has benefits. You will learn a lot about her – your yoni – in either case.

Embodiment practice – Map your yoni

If you want to map your yoni by yourself, you will need a long, penis-shaped object or dildo. And 'long' means that you can insert it as far into your yoni as it can go and still have enough of it outside you so that you can hold it comfortably.

1. Enjoy a short self-pleasuring ritual and get yourself somewhat aroused. Make sure you are wet enough or otherwise use a good-quality lube.
2. Now, imagine your yoni is a clock face with the opening being the center. Twelve o'clock is at the top where your pubic bone is and six o'clock is at the bottom pointing towards your anus.
3. Insert the dildo about two centimeters into your yoni and place its 'head' upwards towards the twelve o'clock position. Push the dildo slightly into the flesh of your yoni.
4. Hold it there for one to two minutes. While doing this, you might experience some physical pain, strong emotions or numbness that may frustrate you. Express whatever comes up for you through sounds and words. You might have random words pop up like 'cold,' 'yellow' or 'tree.' My lover had the word 'broccoli' come up at

a certain spot. Remember, your yoni does not need to make sense. Just be present and keep expressing what comes up.

5. Next, move the head of the dildo towards the one o'clock position, still only inserted about two centimeters. Hold it there for one to two minutes and see what's there.
6. Continue this process around the entire face of the 'clock' until you get back to twelve o'clock.
7. Then insert the dildo a bit deeper inside your yoni and gently press it against the twelve o'clock position at this depth. Hold it for one to two minutes and see what is there.
8. You get the idea ... continue the process around the clock face again at this depth. You can go around as many times as you like at different depths in your yoni.
9. You might experience pleasure and even an internal orgasm but don't be attached to any outcome. The important thing is that you keep going and bring touch and awareness to all areas of your yoni.
10. When you finish, allow yourself a few minutes to rest and integrate this practice. Write down your experiences in your orgasmic diary.

This is a simple yet very powerful exercise that is healing for your yoni and can expand your orgasmic experience. In your first few months of practice, consider doing this type of yoni massage once or twice a week. You can also do this during your daily self-love practice. *(see Diagram 4 on page 99)*

Mapping your yoni

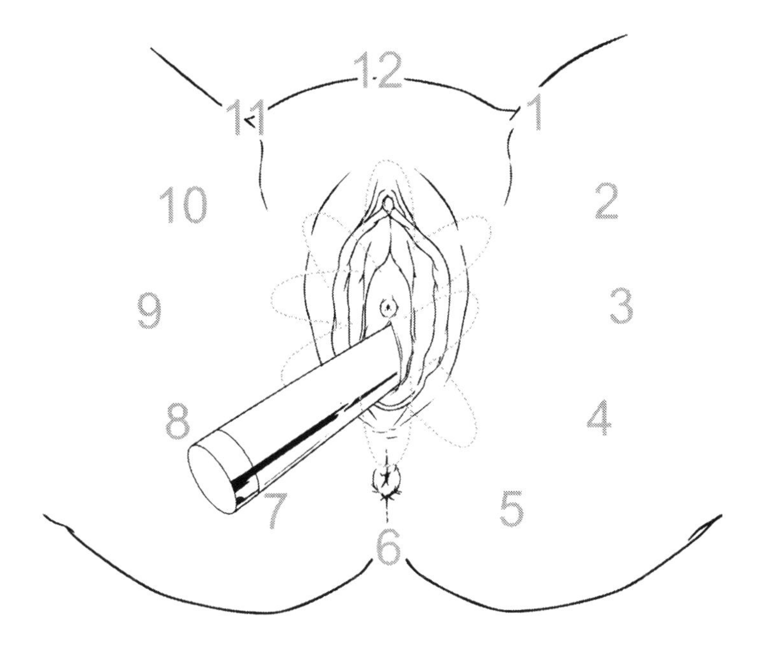

Diagram 4

Orgasmic extras

If you want more ideas about how to express and release emotions, you can check out 'Seven effective ways to deal with emotions' in the resources section of my website (www.intimatepower.com/orgasm-book-resources).

Healing begins with you

Truly loving your vagina means that you know her well and accept her completely. You are sensitive to her needs and desires and you respond accordingly. You love how she looks, smells and tastes. You explore your pleasure externally and internally. You are intimately connected to every part of her. This kind of self-love supercharges your feminine essence, your sexuality and your orgasmic experience. Being fully empowered in this way opens the portal for you to experience orgasm in all manner of ways.

It is critically important to develop self-love and acceptance on your orgasmic journey. This includes pleasuring yourself and embracing your beautiful yoni. If you limit yourself in this area, your orgasmic potential may also be limited. If you don't find the time to do this, it's as if you're saying, 'All of these other things are more important than me, more important than my femininity, my sexuality and my health.' So find the time for yourself.

These practices will help you feel better about your femininity, your body and yourself. You will feel more pleasure and become more orgasmic. Your sex life will improve. And all of these changes will have a noticeable effect on your relationship, creativity, career, friendships, spiritual practice and even financial abundance. Commit to including these practices in your daily and weekly practice, in the same way that you schedule work meetings, picking up your kids from school or going to the gym.

At times it might not be easy. Stuff will come up. You might get frustrated because you're not getting the results you expected or getting them as quickly as you wanted to. Let go of these expectations and keep going with your practice. Rest assured that if you persist, you will reap the orgasmic rewards.

And there are more ways to deal with the challenges and limitations that affect your ability to orgasm. Read on to discover how.

Letting go of limitations

In this part of the book, we will explore the limitations that can affect your ability to orgasm. These limitations are often related to your personal history, upbringing, beliefs and current tendencies. These limitations affect not only your orgasmic capacity, but also other aspects of your life.

If you experience a limited orgasmic ability because of sexual trauma, you will want to seek additional support. There are many professionals who can help you, including myself. While this book intends to optimize your orgasmic experience by yourself, there are some things that are beyond its scope. It can still be a valuable first step, however.

How do you deal with sexual issues?

Self-reflection: *How have you previously dealt with any sexual issues you have experienced?*

Most men in the world easily reach orgasm. You've probably experienced a few that came too easily ... However, many women have difficulty reaching orgasm, and some don't orgasm at all. One of the reasons for this is that women are presented with so much conflicting advice, causing many to give up and not take any action at all.

If you have difficulty reaching deep, satisfying orgasms or if you have other issues with sex, you might be presented with a range of advice from well-meaning people:

- Your priest might say, 'It's a sin to even talk about it.'
- Your mum might say, 'Don't worry about orgasms. They will come one day. The important thing is that you have a husband and kids.'
- Your girlfriends might say, 'The problem is with your man. He doesn't know how to satisfy you. Get yourself a vibrator.'
- Your man may not have a clue at all or perhaps he'll suggest, 'Watch some porn and learn how those actresses do it so easily.'
- Your women's magazine might suggest '10 aphrodisiac foods' or '5 orgasmic sex positions.'
- Your doctor might say, 'You are suffering from a sexual arousal disorder, so take this pill' or 'You have a condition that requires surgery.'
- Your therapist might say, 'To understand your orgasm problem, let's talk about your childhood and sexual history for three months.'
- Your NLP coach might use language to analyze and improve some aspects of your problem.
- Your reiki practitioner might suggest moving the energy in your body.
- Your tantric bodyworker might say, 'You have tension in your vagina, so I will massage your G-spot and all of your problems will be solved.'

So, what do I say?

You are your own healer

I say that you are your own best healer. I say that the strongest transformation comes from your own decision to change your life and from the actions that follow this decision. Becoming more independent and empowered in your sexuality, your relationships and in your life generally all helps.

Imagine you have pain in your back – will you take a painkiller or do you want to try to solve the problem that is causing the pain? My guess is that if the problem persisted, you would go to a massage or bodywork professional, not to a psychologist. But when women have pain in their vagina or issues with their sexual experience, many don't do anything about it and some go to a doctor or a therapist to deal with it. Understanding the cause of a sexual issue might be helpful, but I suggest that talking-therapy by itself is not enough.

The other problem with the different approaches I've mentioned is that most of them come from outside of you – you need to rely on other people, substances or medical procedures to improve your condition. This is very typical of western society – most people look for quick and easy fixes that come from outside and really only address the symptoms.

I believe it's very helpful to see a variety of experienced professionals, as they have the knowledge and techniques that can address various aspects of your problem much more deeply than you can by yourself. However, I recommend you do this alongside your own personal orgasmic journey. The advice you will find in this book will not conflict with any other forms of therapy.

How can your mind help you to orgasm?

I define 'optimal' orgasmic ability as regularly and easily experiencing pleasure and various kinds of orgasms from many kinds of sexual activity, either alone or with a partner. What's interesting is that some women are not bothered or distressed by their lack of pleasure or orgasm, or by a very low frequency of sexual interactions. I've also met many women who simply believed they were incapable of orgasming. Some of them enjoyed sex and experienced some pleasure, but had already accepted the 'fact' that they were never going to orgasm, or *really* orgasm.

The mind is a powerful tool. It can work either with you or against you. I believe that it's important for modern women to know, believe and accept something on the level of the mind before they are able to fully express and embody it. That is why so much of this book is about building knowledge about your body and the amazing orgasms that are possible for you. It's important to remove limiting beliefs about yourself, your body, femininity, sexuality and orgasmic capacity. So, creating new empowering beliefs is what we are about to explore.

Once women are exposed to more knowledge about what's possible and fully understand how their sexuality affects all areas of life, they often decide to focus on their sexuality a bit more. And once they experiment with some of the practices in this book, they start to experience the benefits for themselves. This is why it's important to let go of anything that is limiting your experience of orgasm. Some limiting beliefs include:

- 'I'll never orgasm.'
- 'I can't orgasm because I've been abused.'
- 'Internal orgasms do not exist.'
- 'I'm not meant to orgasm.'
- 'I can't orgasm because I've had a hysterectomy.'
- 'I can't orgasm because my partner's penis is too short or because he comes too quickly.'

- 'I don't orgasm because I'm not _______ enough or because I don't have _______.'
- 'I can't orgasm because that thing happened or didn't happen or because of my partner/kids/work/mother.'

You can let go of your limiting beliefs, but before you set out to change or fix anything, it's important to look at where they came from. What life events, circumstances and conditions have affected you and influenced your beliefs around your sexuality?

Where do sexual limitations come from?

Limiting beliefs, whether they are based on something real and valid or on something assumed and untrue, create unhelpful tendencies and affect your experience of sex and pleasure. So where do they come from? Well, they are largely informed by our past experiences, including:

- Childhood and upbringing.
- Sexual and relationship history.
- Sexual beliefs and preferences.
- Connection to femininity.
- Lifestyle factors.

I remember my teenage years, when I spent long periods of time masturbating in the shower. My mum would knock on the door and shout out, 'Eyal? Are you okay in there? Do you need a rescue team?' I remember experiencing feelings of guilt and shame, like I had to hide what I was doing, and be quiet and quick. I was torn between the pleasure and the guilt. Maybe you have similar memories?

Experiences such as these deeply affect our sexual life and program us to have guilt and shame around our bodies and our sexuality. We become trained to mute our sounds of pleasure and to criticize others who express their sexuality.

There's an important qualification to make here. *It's completely okay to not like something or to choose not to do it.* My point is, ask yourself if your dislike comes from past trauma or societal conditioning. If it does, it's limiting your orgasmic experience. For example, many women don't like to give oral sex or to be taken from behind because they perceive this as degrading for them. Or maybe they feel they are being used or that they are giving up their power. Perhaps they believe that these are things only the man is supposed to enjoy.

We can trace a lot of these perceptions back to how women are portrayed in the media (movies, porn, and so on) and to how society tells women that they should behave. One example is an episode in *Sex and the City* where Charlotte reveals that her partner wants to have anal sex with her:

> *'And I don't want to be the up-the-butt girl, because I mean … Men don't marry up-the-butt girls. Whoever heard of Mrs Up-the-butt? No, no, no. I can't. I want children and nice bedding and I just can't handle this right now.' (Season 1, episode 4)*

I wonder if Charlotte really didn't like the idea of anal play or if she was more concerned with how she was perceived and her identity as the 'good girl.'

So, a sexual limitation isn't something you just don't like. That comes down to personal preference. It is a belief that influences the roles you play and the stories that you might create to perpetuate those roles.

Every person has a 'story' that they've created about themselves. The story has been shaped by your whole life, everything you have ever experienced, everything you were ever told and everything you have witnessed. Some of these stories are empowering. Others are disempowering.

The story usually describes your beliefs about yourself and can be expressed: 'I am…' or 'I always…' or 'I never…' Sometimes it is about other people: 'Men are…' or 'People always … to me.' And it can be directly about sex, as in 'Sex is dirty' or 'Sex doesn't feel good' or 'I don't really need sex.' A story might sound something like, 'Oh I love sex and I love men but I always attract the wrong men. They are always immature and emotionally unavailable.' Or perhaps it goes, 'I hardly ever orgasm, maybe because I was abused as a child.'

There are parts of your story that might be true. For example, that you were abused as a child. And some aspects are simply untrue assumptions and limiting beliefs. For example, 'I'm not meant to orgasm.' Whichever the case, these limiting beliefs often provide some kind of superficial benefit or reward that makes them easy to hold on to.

What you are getting out of your 'story'

The superficial benefits and rewards of something limiting are also known as 'secondary gains.' For example, the secondary gains for a smoker might be experiencing relaxation, the security of routine, the physiological effects of smoking or a feeling of acceptance and belonging. But these secondary gains overlook the main issue – the smoker's health is severely affected and degraded!

People often use the secondary gains of their limiting beliefs as justifications or excuses not to engage in sex and intimacy. The story becomes an excuse to avoid facing your condition and taking action. Your story or your problem will be satisfying some of your basic needs, according to human-needs psychology that was developed by Tony

Robbins and Cloe Madanes. The secondary gains could be one or more of the following:

- Certainty

  As the saying goes, 'Better the devil you know.' Perhaps you have lived with your problem or story for years, maybe decades. You have regular patterns of thought, speech and behavior around it that give you a feeling of certainty and security. For example, as long as you have a problem with sex, you can stay in the state of being single and not risk rejection or a broken heart.

- Uncertainty, novelty or excitement

  Too much certainty gets boring after a while. People need to change their emotional state. Although you know your problem well, it is a constant source of emotions, drama and new problems. For example, 'I had great sex with this guy but now I feel used. Men are such assholes. I feel like shit!' That drama gives you some kind of enjoyment and satisfaction.

- Significance

  Having a problem and a story that explains that problem gives you a sense of significance and importance, first in your own eyes, then in the eyes of others. You feel seen and acknowledged for having a problem. For example, 'My family background was so abusive. No one understands what that is like.'

- Love and connection

  The problem and story combination allows you to feel and connect with yourself and also attracts connection in the form of attention and pity from others. The main way you know how to get love is by having a problem. Perhaps you have a girlfriend who constantly calls you and tells you about all of her problems and pains. Do you sometimes do this yourself?

Furthermore, according to human-needs psychology, once something such as a story or a limiting belief meets three needs, you become addicted to it. Does this help you understand why you might have been experiencing the same problems for all these years? If you have a problem and story combination around your sexuality, it probably satisfies enough of your needs to keep you holding on to it. However, your needs are only being met on a low and superficial level:

- You're not getting real security, just a sad and predictable routine.
- The excitement you get is out of worry and drama, not from joy and ecstasy.
- Your feeling of significance is out of being a victim, not a strong, empowered woman.
- The connection you get as a victim is inferior to the love you could be sharing as an empowered woman if you let go of the story.

What kind of benefit or reward are you getting because you don't orgasm? What's the pay-off for not orgasming to your full potential? What challenges are underneath your 'un-orgasmic-ness' that you aren't facing and letting go of? Are you ready to let go of any disempowering stories and create an empowering story?

From limiting beliefs to unlimited orgasms

To let go of your limitations, you need to first recognize that you have a story. In the beginning of this process, you might only be aware of fragments of your story. But gradually, you will catch yourself telling the story to yourself or others.

Try to notice what you are keen to tell others. What do you use to excuse or justify yourself? What do you say as a strategy to get sympathy or attention? What stories do you tell to get others interested in you? Is there a part of you that enjoys telling and re-telling the story?

This is not to say that you can't talk about your life and your experiences with your loved ones. What you want to look out for are stories that you hang on to and that limit you from fully experiencing your sexuality and even your life. The language you use will often be an indicator that there is a limiting belief keeping you stuck in a story.

Avoid 'painted words'

When you use strong, dramatic or charged words and phrases to describe your experiences, sensations and emotions, you end up magnifying them. On the other hand, when you use neutral words, you decrease the emotional intensity and thus the issue is easier to deal with and let go of. For example, when I say the word 'pain,' you might immediately contract and experience negative images, sensations, emotions or memories just from hearing the word. So instead of using pain, there are other words that can be used to describe an experience that are more neutral, such as discomfort, unpleasantness, soreness, irritation or ache.

Instead of saying, 'It's very painful,' you could say, 'It feels very intense or strong.'

Instead of using 'blockage,' you could use 'hurdle' or 'challenge.'

In BDSM practices where partners facilitate what some might call pain, the term used is 'intense sensation.' This is used so there is not an automatic contraction or negative association.

As you work through the following practices to help release any limitations, be mindful to use neutral words in the stories you are ready to let go of. Finally, keep in mind that painted words are different for everyone, depending on word associations. When I use painted words in this book that have a negative association for you, you can translate them in your mind into more neutral words.

Embodiment practice – Recognize your limiting beliefs

Have a think about what issues and challenges you are facing around your sexuality, relationships, femininity or relating with men as friends or lovers. Why did you choose to read this book about orgasms? What limits you in this area of your life?

This practice has two parts to it:

- First you'll write down all of the limiting beliefs you have about your capacity to orgasm – by yourself, with another person or from any kind of sexual activity.
- Then you'll look at the ways these beliefs are stopping you from enjoying orgasm, your body, sex, relationships and even your life.

Orgasmic extras

If you aren't sure what your limiting beliefs and tendencies are, I have created a *Sexual Self-enquiry Questionnaire* to help you pinpoint anything that is limiting your orgasmic experience. The questionnaire is accompanied by explanations to help your understanding of how your beliefs or tendencies are related to your current sexual expression.

The *Sexual Self-enquiry Questionnaire* is included in the online resources section on my website (www.intimatepower.com/orgasm-book-resources).

1. List as many unhelpful tendencies and limiting beliefs as you can that you have about yourself, your body, your genitals, your femininity, your orgasmic experience, your sexuality, your relationships, and so on. These are thoughts that may run through your mind either generally or when you are in a sexual situation.

2. Frame any thoughts or beliefs you think of as: 'I am…' or 'I always…' or 'I can't…' or 'My…' For example, 'I can't orgasm' or 'I am not worthy of love' or 'My life is fucked up because this and that happened' or 'My body is unattractive.'

3. Next, list your beliefs about other people. Frame these as: 'Men are…' or 'Women are…' or 'My mother…' For example, 'Men are abusive.' Write as many as you can.

4. Take a look at all of the limiting beliefs you've identified. See if you can connect these to any issues, problems and challenges in your life. Try to answer the following questions at length:

   - How do these beliefs affect your relationship and family life?
   - How do these beliefs affect your happiness and fulfillment?
   - How do these beliefs affect your health?
   - How do these beliefs affect your studies, career or creativity?
   - How do these beliefs affect your friendships?
   - How do these beliefs affect your personal and spiritual growth?
   - What other areas or aspects of your life do these problems affect, either directly or indirectly?

   For example, you might identify something like, 'Being unorgasmic and unsure of myself as a woman lowers my confidence with clients, which affects how much money I'm making. This increases my stress levels, my lifestyle, my health and other areas.'

5. Go over everything that you have written and notice any patterns, tendencies or connections between these beliefs and different life events. What did you attract into your life to help you affirm and sustain these beliefs?

When you are able to recognize your limiting beliefs around orgasming, you have already taken a step towards changing them. Bringing the light of consciousness and the focus of awareness to your stories starts the process of letting them go.

Embodiment practice – Feel your resistance

The beliefs you identified in the previous practice may have served you in some superficial way in the past (remember, secondary gains). Maybe they gave you an excuse not to be vulnerable, not to face things that you haven't dealt with or not to express emotions you've suppressed. So what you want to do instead is find empowering and sustainable ways to fulfill your needs.

But there is a part of you that holds on to the 'story' and, therefore, sabotages your happiness and growth. Author Steven Pressfield calls this 'the resistance.' So let's work with your resistance for a moment.

1. Become aware of your resistance towards trying something, doing something or sharing something. Be aware of the voice in your head that might tell you, 'I don't want to masturbate' or 'I don't want to go out and meet people' or 'I don't want to make love with my partner.'

2. Notice how this resistance can stop you from being who you really are. Do you sometimes know what you need to do but don't do it? Do you sometimes do something you know is not good for you?

3. The resistance is afraid of change. The resistance tries to keep you small and disempowered so you don't have to deal with stepping into your greatness. Identify the resistance as something which

isn't you, isn't the real you. Dis-identify with the resistance and it will be easier not to listen to it. Instead of running away to food, Facebook, work, television, sleep or even friends – stay with the resistance without fighting it.

4. Then, allow yourself to take small steps, even tiny steps, towards the thing that you are resisting. If the resistance is telling you not to masturbate, put your hand on your yoni for a few minutes. If the resistance is telling you that you need to eat that cake to feel good, wait a few minutes before eating it.
5. Learn to recognize resistance again and again, whenever you notice your mind affirming your limiting beliefs. Don't fight your mind, just recognize the beliefs as illusions and take steps towards challenging them. Although this might seem like an exercise of the mind, notice what emotions and even bodily responses it brings up within you.
6. Find one action you can take today to demonstrate you are ready for a new belief.

The resistance is what's stopping you from being your full, orgasmic and happy self. So make a commitment to notice the stories and face the resistance – it will enable you to fully become your true self!

Embodiment practice – What's the worst-case scenario?

Issues or challenges that you don't deal with can become worse as time goes by, and they might start to affect other areas of your life too. Most people use positive thinking to shield themselves from the pain and the severity of a challenging situation. However, this is a delusion and an escape mechanism. To develop a strong impetus to change, you need to be aware of the pain that staying the same will bring. This also allows you to visualize the immense pleasure that taking action and changing your ways may result in.

Think about the stories and tendencies that you recognized earlier. How have they affected your life? How have they affected your sex life and your orgasmic experience? How have they affected your current relationship, your family life, health, wealth, friendships and fulfillment in life? How have they stopped you from doing what you want and love?

We are going to explore the worst-case scenario in this practice and then explore the best-case scenario.

1. In ten years, what will your life look like if your problems and beliefs stay the same or get worse? This is not the time for positive thinking or optimism. You really need to have a glimpse of how *bad* things could get. Assume the worst.

2. How will your sexual issues affect your relationship, family life, happiness, fulfillment, health, studies, career, creativity, friendships, personal and spiritual growth?

    - How will you look and feel?

    - Will you have a partner? What kind of a man will he be? What will your relationship be like? Will you have kids? What will your relationship with your kids look life?

    - What will you be doing as a career and how will you feel in your job or business? Will you be financially independent? What kind of house will you be living in?

    - What will you be doing in your free time? Who will your friends be? What would they say about you?

    - What will your health be like?

    Write your very worst-case scenario down in detail. As hard and awful as this might feel, really go into it. Suspend your positive thinking. Assume the worst. Assume every problem and issue you have now will get much worse.

3. Now, notice that some of your worst-case scenario is already somewhat true now. This is proof that your worst-case scenario might actually happen.

4. Allow yourself to feel the pain and suffering associated with this possibility. Feel the pain that you will feel if you actually live your worst-case scenario. What do you feel? How does it feel in your body? Write that in your orgasmic diary.

5. Before you continue to the next practice, take a few minuets to dissolve the strong and heavy energy of the worst-case scenario. Jump and shake for a few minutes. Take a shower. Take a walk outside and get some fresh air.

In order to change, it's important to start recognizing how your past thinking and actions have affected you and could continue to worsen if you do nothing about them. Allow yourself to feel the pain that your limiting beliefs have caused you. This will make it easier for you to take action and change your ways where it will serve you better to do so.

Embodiment practice - Creating the best-case scenario

Now that you have explored the worst things that could happen and felt the pain of this, let's have a look at the other side of the coin – the best things that could happen if you are prepared to take action.

Now is the time for some positive visualization!

1. In ten years time, what will your life look like if you are able to change your limiting beliefs and unhelpful tendencies? What will happen when you solve your problems or overcome your challenges? Positive thinking time! Don't limit the possibilities here. Allow yourself to create the ideal best-case scenario for your life. Allow yourself to wish for the best for yourself. Go for it!

2. How will the very-best-case scenario affect your relationship, family life, happiness, fulfillment, health, studies, career, creativity, friendships, personal and spiritual growth?

3. Close your eyes and take time to build a scenario. See a clear picture of the best future that you could possibly have. Then open your eyes and write it down in detail.

4. Notice how you are feeling about this possible future. Allow yourself to express your feelings through your face and body. Throw your hands in the air and shout, 'YES! I deserve to live the best life!'

5. Now, on a scale of one to ten (with ten being the most committed), how committed are you to making some changes? How inspired are you to make sure you don't end up in the worst-case scenario and, instead, manifest or even exceed your best-case scenario?

If you aren't feeling committed to change at the end of this practice, maybe you are not fully aware of the effects that your sexuality has on your whole life. Perhaps you think you don't have the time, ability, resources or support to be able to change. It's hard to feel committed to something that you regard as impossible.

This practice assumes that everything is possible – and freeing yourself of limitations is what actually opens up all of these possibilities. I've seen women with horrible histories of abuse who have managed to transform their lives and become more feminine, sexual and orgasmic. They have been able to begin having fun sexually as well as develop meaningful relationships with strong, conscious men. This is possible for you too. If you still don't feel totally committed to do everything you can to create the necessary changes in your life, may I suggest that you re-do the worst case scenario practice and this time really allow yourself to consider the worst, then re-do the best case scenario practice and allow yourself to specify what is it you really yearn for.

Embodiment practice – Affirm your orgasmic ability

Many women continue to affirm their limiting beliefs. 'I'm not feeling anything' or 'It hurts' or 'I'm not orgasmic' or 'I never orgasm.' So these beliefs become, or remain, their reality. But if you have recognized your limiting beliefs and have decided to let them go, you need to create a set of empowering beliefs phrased as intentions, positive statements or affirmations.

1. Come up with positive affirmations that are in in no way limiting. For example:
    - 'I'm worthy of love.'
    - 'I love my self, my body, my genitals and my sexuality.'
    - 'It's okay to feel, express and let go.'
    - 'I am a sexual woman.'
    - 'I am an orgasmic woman.'

Also come up with affirmations according to your specific situation.

2. Choose three affirmations that are the most meaningful, inspiring or charged for you. Write your three selected affirmations in your orgasmic diary. Consider sticking them to your mirror, laptop, windscreen or smartphone.
3. Vocalize your affirmations every morning and whenever you are feeling fear or doubt.
4. Repeat your selected affirmations while you self-pleasure or when you are in another high-energy state, such as when dancing, exercising or making love. Using the energy of orgasm, pleasure or dance will help you manifest these affirmations.

Be mindful that positive thinking alone doesn't work. For example, the movie called *The Secret* presented a very simplistic and delusional picture of positive thinking. People who watched it believed that you just have to visualize a million dollar check and it would naturally appear the next day. It doesn't work like that.

Positive affirmations don't work if you have negative thoughts and emotions that are stronger than the positive messages. Or perhaps you have tendencies and behavior patterns that negate the positive affirmations. So, a thought by itself isn't enough. It needs to be accompanied by positive actions and, moreover, the right actions. There are plenty of practices included in this book that will help you here.

You can also use the power of open questions to reframe your limiting beliefs if they are still stronger than your positive affirmations. Try turning your problem statements into open questions. Instead of saying, 'I can't orgasm,' ask, 'How can I orgasm?' Instead of saying 'I can't lose weight,' ask, 'How can I lose weight?' Open questions don't create an internal conflict and will instead invite curiosity, exploration and flexibility that will also assist you to take empowering action.

Embodiment practice – Visualize an amazing sex experience

Visualization is another way you can use your mind as a powerful tool to create sexual energy or heal your past wounds. Visualization begins with the mind but then creates a real effect in your body. So in the beginning you might be 'just imagining,' but soon you will be able to actually feel it. Here are two ways you can try this:

- Visualize what amazing sex would feel like. Describe the physical attributes and character of your partner. Describe the feelings, emotions and sensations you perceive through all five senses. Write this down.
- Write a description of one of your fantasies. Don't try to make it nice. It doesn't need to be 'spiritual' or 'artistic' or 'poetic' or

'feminine' or even 'sensual.' Just start writing. For example, 'I touch my nipple ... I feel this ... I do this ... He does that ... I can feel my heart pulsating ... His hard-on is pressing against my thigh ... I can feel my pussy getting wet,' and so on. Describe your perception through your five senses as well as your feelings, emotions, thoughts, associations and memories.

While visualization is a powerful tool on the way to stronger pleasure and orgasms, it's important to cultivate awareness and connection to the present moment and the person you are actually with. Make sure you don't use visualization when you're making love with another person. You can experiment with visualization when you self-pleasure but try to focus on the sensations and feelings in your body and stay connected to these.

Other orgasmic inhibitors

Limiting beliefs are a major inhibitor of a woman's orgasmic ability but there are other factors and experiences that can affect this as well. Sometimes these factors can even become the seed of a limiting belief. Let's talk through a few so that you know what to look out for.

Do you have any sexual fantasies that you consider 'dirty' or 'wrong'?

Most people, both women and men, have sexual fantasies that they feel bad about. This is another kind of limiting belief, causing guilt or shame and subsequently limiting your sexual expression.

The most common of these is a rape fantasy – either raping or being raped. According to studies conducted from 1973 through to 2008, forty per cent of the women surveyed had a rape fantasy about once a month. I believe that the actual figure is higher or more frequent than this because most women do not feel comfortable admitting to this fantasy. More women will admit to wanting to be 'overpowered' but shy away from admitting the rape fantasy.

The crucial thing to understand is: *This fantasy does not mean they actually want to get raped!*

A rape fantasy symbolizes a woman's yearning to go into her feminine, to surrender and let go completely with a man who is fully masculine. She wants to let go of the need to control or decide and be totally taken, lead and contained by a man she totally trusts. So if you have these kinds of fantasies, know that you are normal and many women around you have similar fantasies.

It's important to acknowledge the yearning to let go of control and surrender. You can start exploring this in your sex life as well as in your professional, creative, social and spiritual life. You can let go of control and allow people you trust to guide you and take care of you. This doesn't mean that you're weak. On the contrary, you can only truly surrender from a place of power.

Orgasmic extras

If you are concerned by rape fantasies, you can read more about these here: www.psychologytoday.com/blog/all-about-sex/201001/womens-rape-fantasies-how-common-what-do-they-mean

Are you subject to a lot of stress at work or at home?

Stress is one of the biggest factors that can hurt your ability to orgasm. To have deep and meaningful orgasms, you need to be comfortable and relaxed.

Do you sometimes feel depressed? Or do you take antidepressants?

Depression affects your ability to orgasm and while antidepressants can help with depressive feelings, they also impact your ability to orgasm. Specifically, selective serotonin re-uptake inhibitors (SSRI) hurt your sex drive and your ability to orgasm. Antidepressants have many other side effects too, such as nausea, insomnia, dizziness, weight gain or loss, tremors, anxiety, restlessness, drowsiness, fatigue, dry mouth, diarrhea or constipation, headaches, etcetera (all of which can further exacerbate depression).

As a result, I believe many people would be better served by holistic and alternative medicine than by being dependent on chemicals and seeing therapists for years. Gradually getting off medication and working on your femininity, sexuality and orgasm can help to relieve or even cure depression. Disclaimer: I'm not a doctor. Most doctors will not support this belief. Make sure you make the right decision for yourself and that you have friends who can support you and look after you during any transition phase.

My point is that depression hurts orgasm but *orgasm can help your depression.*

Are you on the pill?

How many years have you been taking it? Did you feel any effects when you started taking it? Women are highly susceptible to their hormones and messing with these hormones can mess with more aspects of your life than you may think.

The contraceptive pill is a bit of a blessing and a curse. Sure, when used correctly, it allows you to have unprotected sex with very little risk of getting pregnant. But it also has side effects that include vaginal dryness, decreased libido, lower arousal and diminished ability to orgasm. Some women report that when they go off the pill, they not only have more sensation but they also feel a greater connection with their body and their femininity.

Another very important side effect that the pill has is that it affects the woman's connection to her intuition about potential partners. Some women have shared that when they got off the pill, they discovered they were no longer attracted to their partners. And some discovered this after they were already married or pregnant ... or both.

Have you ever gone through an abortion?

Abortion can create a kind of trauma on the physical, energetic, emotional, mental and spiritual levels. The medical procedure can cause guilt, physical distress and pain. Also, the bureaucratic process subjects a woman to the attitudes of the medical staff and other people. This all has an effect on a woman's sexuality. I once went through an abortion process with my partner and, even as a man, it wasn't easy. I can't imagine how it would feel for a woman.

Have you had any kind of genital, abdominal or reproductive surgery?

Any kind of surgery in the area of the genitals and lower belly might sever important nerves that lead to and from the genitals. Many doctors aren't even aware of the structure or importance of these nerves. The result for some women who go through a caesarean operation or other kinds of surgery is a loss of some subtle sensation and pleasure in their genital area.

Have you experienced sexual abuse?

Have you had any kind of unwanted touch or sex from either a stranger or someone you knew? Did it happen more than once? Was it before puberty? Any kind of sexual abuse affects a woman's femininity, sexuality, ability to orgasm and ability to function in a relationship.

The worst kind of abuse is that committed by a family member before puberty, during a child's formative years. This sets very deeply into the child's subconscious and affects how they relate to themselves and to the world around them.

However, it's also important to remember that even women who have experienced abuse in their childhood or later in life have healed to become sexual, orgasmic, loving, open, strong and successful. Acknowledge whatever you went through, but see how anything else you might be faced within your life pales in comparison to what you have already experienced. You survived and this has the potential to make you stronger.

Orgasmic extra

For a longer list of factors that might be limiting your orgasmic experience, check out *The new view of sexual disorders* in the online resources section on my website (www.intimatepower.com/orgasm-book-resources)

For any experience that is traumatic or inhibits your orgasmic or sexual expression, know that there are people that can help you. You don't have to do it all on your own.

How can others help?

Most of this book shows you how you can heal and pleasure yourself, by yourself. At the same time, it's also beneficial to seek the guidance and help of professionals.

Many therapeutic or psychological traditions put a huge emphasis on where your problems came from – childhood, past trauma, and so on. This can be helpful to an extent but, as we've seen, you need to let go of the story or the limitations to fully move forward. By contrast, alternative healing modalities focus on how to solve the problem you are experiencing in the present even if it is caused by things that happened in the past. This is an important aspect of my 'holistic transformation model' – receive. You can receive help from others. There are plenty of options:

- Your partner/lover/boyfriend/husband

  If you have a partner, share that you are engaging in a journey of orgasmic awakening. Ask for his patience, understanding and support. Explain the types of orgasm you would like to experience and ask him to help you achieve them during lovemaking. Ask him to give you a sensual massage. Invite him to map your yoni with the clock technique. Ask him to refrain from stimulating your clit or to stop when you ask him to, so you don't experience a clitoral orgasm and lose your sexual and vital energy.

  Be with a man who is willing to support you in this way. If a lover isn't willing to do this for you, it's probably a sign that you shouldn't be with him. And don't just receive from him – give him the same support as a part of your process. On a side note, the more you work on yourself, the more you will inspire your partner to care for you and work on himself.

- Friends

  Share your journey and your progress with your close friends. If they are already orgasmic and sexually open, ask them to share advice or experiences. Even if they say something contrary to what is suggested in this book, experiment with both approaches. If you are close with your girlfriends, you might be able to do some of the practices together.

- Counselors, therapists and psychologists

  The best thing you receive from these professionals is having someone really listen to you. Then they can work with you on past traumas and current challenges. However, I find that many psychologists aren't so helpful because they only work with the mind, rather than the holistic nature of the individual. I recommend seeing therapists with a specific knowledge of and experience in sexual therapy. Preferably, use those who work with both the mind and the body, such as body-psychotherapists and somatic-psychologists.

- Life-coaches

  These professionals can help you to develop more clarity around your priorities. They facilitate setting goals and timelines and taking specific actions. They also make you more accountable for your actions and behaviors.

- Sexual healers and coaches

  Sometimes these professionals are known as a daka or a dakini – a sacred intimate or tantric bodywork professional. An experienced sexual healer knows how to touch, arouse, heal and open your body, more so than most men and women. Some sexual healers include genital touch and some don't. Some sexual healers might have sex with their clients. That's legit as long as it's planned and agreed to before the session.

  A sexual healer can be a man, a woman or even a couple. If you find it challenging to work with a man, start by working with a female practitioner. However, I highly recommend following that with a few sessions with a male practitioner because this will be a meaningful step in your healing journey. Generally, I recommend sexual healers who combine bodywork, talk therapy and homework that you do by yourself. If you want to receive support from a sexual healer, you can contact me for a private consultation. I conduct most of my sessions via Skype with people all over the world and get great results, without any physical touch. I may also be able to recommend another legitimate professional suited to your situation.

When you have let go of limiting beliefs, behaviors and experiences around sexuality and orgasm, you are ready to experiment further and explore the practices that can increase your orgasmic ability and experience.

5

Orgasmic power practices

There are some women who naturally orgasm, have multiple orgasms or have long orgasmic states without any effort or techniques. For everyone else, it helps to learn a few techniques and how to relax. Some techniques work better for some women than others. The idea is to explore different things and see what works for you. A technique might feel like an effort at first, which may seem to go against what we have learned about the importance of relaxation on the road to orgasm. But they can help you to learn a new way of being and will gradually become natural and effortless.

It's possible to orgasm just by doing special breathing techniques, producing certain sounds, making specific body movements or using a combination of these things. And if you can relax into an effortless use of technique, it simply takes over without needing to think about it. So aspire to relax and surrender during these practices so that the relaxation and technique becoming one.

This section of the book is a highly practical guide that shares many techniques. We'll look at breath, sound, movement, touch and more. I invite you to experiment with curiosity and openness, either by yourself or with a lover. You never know which technique might power up your orgasm!

Breath

Breath is a basic element that enables you to experience more pleasure and become more orgasmic.

Breath is powerful. It carries oxygen and energy into the body and when it's released, it carries stress out of the body. It can charge you up and rejuvenate you or relax and pacify you. Breath grounds you in your body and makes you more aware of your emotions.

Traditional yoga includes many exercises called 'Pranayamas' that combine breath, energy and mental focus. These exercises allow the yogis to charge their body with energy and raise their level of consciousness.

Self-reflection: *Sit comfortably and take a deep breath. Then take another breath. Notice if your chest and shoulders rise. Notice if your belly expands.*

When I've asked women to take a deep breath during a coaching session, many will breathe strongly into their chest while pulling their bellies in and raising their shoulders up. But this type of breathing creates tension and anxiety because it is connected to a primal instinct to raise our shoulders to protect our neck when we feel threatened.

The media and popular culture have led many women to believe they are supposed to have a concave or toned belly. So many constrict their breath and keep their bellies sucked in. While the lungs don't actually extend into the belly, the movement of the diaphragm naturally pushes the belly out. But instead of breathing into the belly, many women breathe into their chest. Some women will also avoid breathing into their bellies because they are trying to avoid the emotions and memories that are suppressed there. I sometimes have to spend a few sessions coaching a client to change her breathing pattern so as to help her improve her orgasmic experience.

Belly breathing is especially important when it comes to orgasm. It charges the womb and genitals with energy. Breathing into your belly allows you to connect with your body and your femininity and feel your emotions more clearly. Deep breathing raises your level of consciousness and awareness and facilitates healing. I've even met a few women who are able to take a few deep breaths into their bellies and immediately orgasm.

Deep breath = Deep orgasm.

Let's play with breath and you can note what you experience in your orgasmic diary.

Embodiment practice – Belly breath

This practice will allow you to experience the effect of deep belly breathing.

1. Sit or lie down comfortably. Close your eyes and place one hand on your lower belly and the other on your chest.
2. Breathe deeply into your belly, imagining that your lungs are actually extending all the way into your belly.
3. Continue breathing into your belly, inhaling slowly through your nose and exhaling through your mouth.
4. With your hands, feel your lower belly expanding with every breath, and make sure that your chest is not rising and expanding. Allow your lower belly to expand and protrude.
5. Visualize your breath is like warm massage oil caressing your womb, ovaries and vagina.

6. Make sure that you are breathing fully into your lower belly. Do this for five to ten minutes.

7. Then relax your breath, close your eyes and notice how you feel.

Use your journal to record your experience. What sensations did you feel? What emotions or feelings came up? Did any memories or insights come up? How connected do you feel to your body, femininity and sexuality after this practice? Do you feel any different?

Once you get used to breathing to your belly, you are ready to experiment with stronger techniques with more obvious orgasmic benefits.

Embodiment practice – Mouth breathing

This practice energizes your body and specifically charges up your second charka, the sacral or sexual chakra, with energy.

1. Breathe in and out through your mouth taking full belly breaths – similar to the last practice, but inhaling and exhaling only through your mouth and at a much faster pace.

2. Continue this for three to five minutes.

3. Then relax your breath, close your eyes and notice how you feel.

Use your journal to record your experience. What sensations did you feel? What emotions or feelings came up? Did any memories or insights come up? How connected do you feel to your body, femininity and sexuality after this practice? Do you feel any different?

This breathing technique can be used when you self-pleasure or make love. It will enable you to feel more pleasure.

Embodiment practice – Full breath retention

While it's important to breathe fully and regularly, there is also value in learning to control your breath. This practice demonstrates the effect of holding your breath and directing your attention. It will either charge your genitals with energy or otherwise have a calming effect.

1. Inhale fully, filling your abdomen and chest.
2. Hold the breath for as long as you can while focusing on your genitals.
3. Release the breath and then take a few deep breaths.
4. Take another deep breath and hold it as before.
5. Do this five to ten times.

Use your journal to record your experience. What sensations did you feel? What emotions or feelings came up? Did any memories or insights come up? How connected do you feel to your body, femininity and sexuality after this practice? Do you feel any different?

You can experiment with this technique even while you have sex. You'll be surprised by the effect it can have. Once you've practiced holding a full inhalation, it's time to practice the opposite.

Embodiment practice – Void retention

This practice allows you to move your energy away from your genitals towards your upper body and higher chakras. It can also be very relaxing.

1. Inhale fully and then exhale fully, making sure you expel all the air from your lungs.

2. Hold your breath there (while it's expelled) for as long as you can. Focus on the middle of your forehead, the area known in yoga as your third eye or Ajna chakra.
3. Release the breath and then take a few breaths.
4. Do this for five to ten times.

Use your journal to record your experience. What sensations did you feel? What emotions or feelings came up? Do you feel any different?

This practice is a very powerful yogic technique. Doing this every morning and after every sexual experience can help you to have more mental clarity and be less emotional.

Breath is your pathway to orgasm

Breath is a pathway to orgasm. Different kinds of breath have different effects and can trigger different sensations and orgasmic states. It's important that you experiment with all of the above practices so you can enjoy all of their benefits. The more you are connected to your breath, the deeper and easier you can orgasm. And deep breath is necessary to make deep continuous sounds, which are another important part of orgasm.

Sound

Sound is a crucial element for expanding your orgasmic experience, improving your sex life and empowering yourself as a woman.

Sound is related to the throat chakra and, according to Tantra, women generally have less openness in this energy center than men. Even medical studies show more women than men experience problems with throat infections and their thyroid gland, which is located in the throat. Can you see the connection? Having a blockage in your throat chakra is related to a difficulty expressing yourself. This may be with your partner, in your social life or in your professional life. You may have challenges around expressing your feelings, needs, boundaries, emotions, thoughts, opinions and preferences. You might also have difficulty expressing yourself creatively and artistically.

Sound is also related to the third chakra (the navel chakra or Manipura), which is connected to personal power. So expressing sounds also helps you connect to your own power. And this includes your orgasmic power.

Self-reflection: *Think about how you make love. Do you easily make sounds during lovemaking? Do you enjoy making sounds?*

One of the primary techniques I use to help women become more orgasmic is to coach them to express stronger and more frequent sounds. A woman who expresses herself more easily than others will find it easier to make stronger sex sounds. Sound alone can create pleasure sensations and even orgasm. And sound is often the missing link that prevents a woman from orgasming – from *really* orgasming.

Sounds are empowering in many ways

Allowing yourself to make sounds carries many benefits. Some can be immediately experienced during lovemaking and others are more indirect and take time to be noticed. Check out some of the empowering effects you can experience. Sound:

- Leads to more sexual pleasure.
- Makes it easier to orgasm or can bring about your first orgasm.
- Facilitates internal and whole body orgasms.
- Supports the lengthening of orgasms into long orgasmic states.

- Provides more freedom in bed and in life.
- Helps you find your voice in life (many women do not feel 'heard').
- Heals trauma.
- Expresses suppressed emotions.
- Decreases or dissolves guilt and shame around sexuality.
- Helps you become more confident, creative and expressive.

As you can see, expressing yourself through sounds can empower you both sexually and in other areas of your life. Your sounds can also bring pleasure to your partner and make it easier for them to make sounds, just by witnessing you and listening to you. Your sex sounds might even inspire your neighbors! If more people made strong sex sounds, it would become more culturally acceptable to do so.

The power of sound

Sounds are sensual and will enhance your orgasmic experience. The following ideas and attitudes that may help you to express sounds more easily, experience more pleasure and express more aspects of yourself.

1. Every sensation has a sound

   Different sensations have different sounds. Pleasure sounds are different to pain sounds. Rough sounds are different to soft sounds. Experiment with finding and expressing a sound for every sensation you feel. If you don't feel anything, make a bored or frustrated sound.

2. Every emotion and feeling has a sound

   Making sounds isn't just about making pleasure sounds, it's more about expressing whatever comes up for you – pleasure, pain, sadness, anger, frustration, and so on. Joy would sound different to anger or sadness, wouldn't it? So, make different sounds to express the different emotions you feel.

3. Every place in your body has a different sound

   Would touching your thigh produce a different sound to touching your nipple? Does a foot sound different to a yoni? Express different sounds according to the different places in your body that are being touched, or where you feel strong energy or sensations.

4. Different sounds produce different effects

   Sensations, emotions and body parts can trigger particular sounds but this also works the other way around – certain sounds can trigger particular effects. So if you consciously make a specific sound, you can produce a specific effect in your body. Experiment with different kinds of sounds: A short, frequent 'Ahhh' or a long, continuous 'Aaaaaaaaaa,' rising and falling sounds, high- or low-pitch tones, and so on.

5. Sounds don't need a reason

   Take a deep breath and make any sound right now. Why did you make that sound? Most probably because I asked you to and you agreed to – even if you didn't feel anything in that moment. You don't have to wait to be touched or penetrated to make sounds. You don't have to feel pleasure or even anything to make sounds. You can make sounds simply for the sake of making sounds.

Everything has a sound and the more you are able to express sound – the more you can use it to expand your orgasmic experience.

So, what stops you from making sounds?

Obviously, one reason is that you are not feeling any pleasure. And in other cases, pleasure and orgasm can be strong but not be expressed via sounds. It's also good to be open to experiences of silent ecstasy.

But what stops you from making (loud) sounds when you are feeling some pleasure and expressing that would be natural for you? Well, there are a few main reasons that you may relate to:

- Not knowing how to make sounds.
- Not being used to making sounds.
- Being self-conscious about making sounds.
- Being afraid of how you will be perceived by your partner.
- Being afraid of being heard by other adults or children.
- Being afraid of being judged or criticized for having sex or for being sexual.
- Being afraid of being labeled as a 'slut.'
- Feeling guilt and shame about sexuality.
- Having sexual or emotional trauma.
- Growing up in (or still experiencing) circumstances where self-expression isn't allowed – whether that is your needs, emotions, opinions or true self.

Sounds are closely connected to your self-expression and it's important to feel comfortable expressing yourself when you are on an orgasmic journey. The practices that follow will help you to be more free with your voice and sound, and will allow you to unleash your orgasmic power.

The basics of making sounds

Maybe you think you are already making strong sex sounds. Are you sure? Well, let me ask you this:

Have you ever heard a loud knocking from the other side of the wall?

Have your neighbors ever complained?

Did you ever lose your voice after a few hours of lovemaking?

If not, perhaps there is room for a bit more volume or a bit more range, even if you are comfortable making your current sounds. It's worth exploring. I've rarely met an orgasmic woman who didn't make a lot of different sounds. Loud sounds.

So, have a play with the embodiment practices that follow whether you are a 'screamer' or completely silent. These basic reminders will make it easier for you to make sounds as you explore:

- Breathe deeply – Sounds need air. Many women hold their breath when they are aroused or touched. To make sounds, you need to breathe. Deeply.
- Breathe into your belly – It's much easier to make sounds when you breathe deeply in and out of your belly. It's harder if you're breathing to your chest.
- Make sounds mainly through your mouth, not your nose – Making sounds through your mouth creates more openness, expression and freedom. When you are really aroused, your sounds will naturally come more through your mouth.
- Keep your mouth open and your jaw relaxed – If you make sounds through clenched teeth, it feels and sounds different to making sounds through your open mouth. Open your mouth and move your jaw from side to side to relax it. If it looks weird, you're doing it right.

The following practices will help you turn the theory of sound into an expressive reality. You can make the sounds just because, or you can do so while you are self-pleasuring or having sex. If possible, try both.

Embodiment practice – Find sounds to express words

This practice allows you to express different emotions with sounds and can make it easier to express yourself if the emotion is challenging for you.

1. Prepare a list of words that connect to different aspects of sex and pleasure. Here are a few suggestions:
   - Soft and tender
   - Strong and intense
   - Wild
   - Feminine
   - Innocent
   - Sensual
   - Kinky
   - Sacred
2. Ask yourself, 'If this word had a sound, what would the sound be?' Take a minute or two to find a sound that expresses each of these words.
3. Next, take a few minutes to explore different aspects of each sound. Have fun with it. Play. Go crazy. Pretend. Experiment.

When you're finished with each sound, take a moment to note how you feel and write it down in your orgasmic diary. It's also important to notice which sound (if any) challenged you or was hard to make.

This practice helps you to get used to making sounds according to what you are feeling. And if you have issues with a particular sound, the next practice can help with that.

Embodiment practice – What sound are you avoiding?

You may find there are sounds you avoid during self-pleasure or sex. Maybe you found a couple in the previous practice. Ask yourself, 'What sound do I avoid?' or 'What sound am I afraid to make?' or 'What sound am I challenged by?' or even 'This sound is silly/ugly/boring/crazy,' and so on.

1. When you find a sound you are avoiding, make that sound for a few minutes. If you have a problem with a certain sound, it might mean that you have an issue with or a resistance to an aspect of femininity or sexuality and that probably affects a similar aspect in your daily life. So go back to the sounds that challenged you.
2. Try to express the challenging sounds as well as any emotions they are connected to. Keep trying to express these sounds, even if you feel that you're 'faking it' at first.
3. Notice what comes up for you and write it down in your orgasmic diary.

This practice will enhance your sex life by embracing different energies and emotions via the sounds you make. And this will affect other aspects of your life too.

Embodiment practice – Different sounds have different effects

As we discussed earlier, different sounds have different effects. If you consciously make a specific sound, you can produce a specific effect in your body. This practice helps you to explore how sounds affect you in different ways.

Take a few minutes to experiment with each of the sounds listed below. Note how each one makes you feel and write it down in your orgasmic diary.

- Air sound – The sound of air passing through your throat and mouth. You can aim to make this sound continuously whenever you're not making another sound.
- Sigh – Slightly louder than the air sound. Make a sigh to suit whatever sensation or emotion you're experiencing.
- 'Ah' sound – A short and strong 'ah' sound, as in, 'ah … ah … ah …'
- 'Aaaaaaah' sound – A long and continuous 'Aaaaaaah' sound, which is related to the heart chakra. Take a deep breath and then when you exhale, make the continuous sound. This makes long sounds easier. Then, make the same sound but louder and louder, while still keeping it long.
- Falling 'ah' sounds – Imagine coming back home after a long hard day, sinking into the couch or a hot bath and making a sound. That would usually sound like a falling 'ah' sound. It expresses relief and relaxation.
- Crying sound – Making the same sounds you make (or used to make as a child) when you cry.
- Growling – Imagine you're an animal. What sounds would an animal make when she's on heat? Also, imagine you're a male animal. What sounds would he make?
- High-pitch sounds – These are the highest sounds you are able to make.
- Low-pitch sounds – These are the lowest sounds you can make and will feel like they're coming from your belly.
- Shouting and screaming – The stronger you express sound, the more effect it will have. If it's possible, allow yourself to really shout and scream loudly. You can use a pillow to muffle the sound if you feel that is appropriate.

When you're finished experimenting with all of these sounds, go back to the sounds that challenged you, as discussed earlier. Incorporate some or all of these sounds into your self-pleasuring, your love-making and even throughout your day. It will help with your self-expression in all areas of your life, deepen your pleasure and make you more confident.

Embodiment practice – Say 'YES!' to your pleasure

If you have some reservations around making sounds, it's important to create the conditions that will allow you to make sounds more freely. Many women avoid making sounds because they are afraid of being heard. What will the neighbors say? What will people think?

If this is inhibiting you, there are a few ways you can muffle your sounds so that you feel more freedom to experiment:

- Close all the doors and windows.
- Shout into a thick pillow.
- Shout into the mattress.
- Turn on the vacuum cleaner or some music.
- Practice at a time where people are away, for example during the morning hours.
- Make sounds in the car.
- Rent a secluded hut or go camping.

Whatever way you can manage to make loud sounds, keep using it during self-pleasuring and love-making. Once you learn how to make strong sounds, it's important to incorporate it into your sexual practice. Perhaps you will allow yourself to be a 'screamer'?

1. Have a self-pleasuring session where you keep making loud sounds. Really allow yourself to make all the sounds you always

wanted to make. Incorporate whatever other techniques that you like from this book.

2. Remember that every sensation has a sound and try to give sounds to the range of sensations and emotions you experience. If you don't know what the sound is, go with a long 'aaaaaaah' or invent a sound.
3. If you are feeling pleasure, exaggerate your sound and lengthen it. Even when you feel your pleasure dropping, keep making sounds.
4. I also invite you to play with the word 'yes.' This is one of the most important sounds you can make. So, go for it. Pleasure yourself and make sounds the entire time. And don't forget to include, 'Yes ... yes ... yes ... OH YESSSSSS!'
5. After you finish, note in your orgasmic diary how this self-pleasure practice was different than before.

I often instruct clients to repeatedly say 'yes' as I massage, de-armor or stimulate them. Why is 'yes' so important? Well, when you say the word 'yes,' you are saying yes to the present moment and whatever it brings. You say yes to any pain, yes to any pleasure and yes to healing yourself. During sex, you say yes to sex, yes to being a woman, yes to your man and yes to life. When you say 'yes' repeatedly, you program your subconscious to understand that whatever you're doing is good for you and you want it. So this is especially powerful during self-pleasure or sex.

Maybe in the past you wanted to say 'no' but you were forced or coerced. This practice is your chance to choose 'yes.' To affirm that you are a sexual woman and you have every right to touch yourself, to have sex and to experience pleasure.

Saying 'yes' during sex also gives your partner an indication that what he or she is doing is good for you. So if they are doing something that you enjoy and you say yes, there's more chance that they will keep doing it! And as a man, it feels great to hear a woman say, 'YES!'

This practice is a foundational self-pleasure technique. Whenever possible, always include sounds and use the word 'yes,' both in and out of the bedroom.

How 'faking it' can sometimes serve you

Women who regularly fake orgasms actually hurt their ability to orgasm. Instead of pausing and saying, 'This isn't working for me. It's painful. I don't feel anything,' or whatever is unpleasing for her, she pretends that everything is good. This can reinforce limiting beliefs such as, 'I don't deserve to be loved' or 'I can't orgasm.'

Faking it in this way also perpetuates a dynamic with your partner that disempowers him since he's not aware that what he is doing isn't pleasuring you and might actually be painful. This can further impact you because you're left with a feeling of guilt over faking it, bitterness and frustration over not feeling pleasure, and even anger and sadness with yourself, your partner or life generally. This is not a good recipe for orgasm, a happy relationship or a fulfilling life.

Maybe you also 'fake it' in your daily life – pretending that you like something or someone when you actually don't. Trying to do and say the right thing and avoid saying the wrong thing. Trying to fit in and be loved, validated and accepted. As I mentioned earlier, everything is connected and anything you do privately also projects out and influences your life publicly. So faking orgasms isn't a good idea. You obviously want to experience real orgasms, not fake ones!

However, it's possible to 'fake' pleasure and orgasm as a technique or a trick for yourself to help bring about a real orgasm. You see, in some ways, your brain is like someone locked in a room who perceives the external world by the messages that are delivered via the senses. When you deliver the right kind of messages to your brain, you can trick your brain into believing you are having an orgasm. Then your brain will send the messages to your body that create an actual orgasm. *This is the only way you want to fake it!*

Sometimes, during a sexual healing session, I instruct a woman to fake orgasm sounds or say 'I'm coming.' Often she will tell me, 'I'm feeling some pleasure, but I'm not really coming.' I instruct her to make the sounds anyway, like a game. After a few minutes of doing this and shouting, 'Yes! Yes! I'm coming!' something changes in her sounds and movements. Then she says, 'I'm coming! ... I mean, I'm *really* coming!'

Embodiment practice – Fake it till you make it

Will this work for you? There's only one way to find out – so give it a try! Start a self-pleasuring ritual with internal stimulation as discussed earlier. From the very beginning, experiment with the following:

1. Intensify and exaggerate everything you feel by expressing it with sounds stronger than how it actually feels.
2. Pretend you are someone else that you imagine would make sex sounds freely – Marilyn Monroe, Madonna, Beyoncé or a porn star. Move, touch yourself and make sounds as if you were her.
3. After you get somewhat aroused, keep exaggerating your movements and making strong sounds continuously. Moan. Shout, 'Yes! I'm coming!' You might feel silly or self-conscious but remember you are playing a game and having fun. Keep going.
4. Occasionally, pause and notice the sensations you are experiencing. Then keep going, incorporating the ideas and sounds we covered earlier.

5. Do this for ten to fifteen minutes, then completely relax and note how you're feeling. Write your experiences in your orgasmic diary.

This is a great practice to try and do occasionally, and it might allow you to try things you haven't done before or even trick your subconscious into believing you are actually orgasming. However, remember not to fake your orgasm on a regular basis or with your partner. It is best to use this alone as a technique to help unleash your orgasm.

You can use sounds to encourage orgasmic effects in your body. And when your body feels orgasmic, it wants to move in an orgasmic way. So let's explore how movement can help to you to unleash your orgasm.

Movement

Movement is one of the key elements that can enhance and even transform your experience of sex, orgasm and life in general. There are so many ways that moving your body can benefit you. Here are just a few. Movement:

- Charges your whole body with blood, oxygen and energy.
- Dissolves any physical, energetic and emotional blocks.
- Releases stagnant energy in your genitals, joints, sacrum, spine and other areas.
- Takes you out of a bad mood and facilitates joy and satisfaction (owing to the endorphins released during exercise).
- Takes you out of your head (over-thinking) and into your body and the present moment.
- Helps you connect to, appreciate and love your body.
- Enables experience of higher states of arousal (this can be experienced by women after mild cardio exercise).

- Creates a physical vibration and friction that can activate and arouse the genitals.
- By itself can create pleasure and orgasm.
- Helps you to relax during sexual activity.
- Makes it easier to internalize clitoral stimulation.
- Facilitates whole-body pleasure and orgasm.
- Makes you feel more free and uninhibited during sex and in life.
- Dissolves guilt and shame around femininity, your body, sexuality and pleasure .
- Connects you deeper to your femininity, womanhood and your 'Shakti' (the Sanskrit term for the divine feminine).

Yet even though movement has all of these benefits, many women don't know how to move during sex or are afraid to do so. Some women just lie there and expect their partner to do everything. But movement affects the woman's pleasure and her partner's. It brings pleasure to a man, first just by looking at you, and then by being next to you and inside you.

Moving your body in a sensual way has a subconscious effect much like sound does. When you move in a way that feels sexy and good, you are connecting to your inner seductress or temple dancer. Generally speaking, I have found that the more a woman knows how to move during sex, the more orgasmic she is. So on this note, let's look at some practices that can free up your movement and help you to feel more orgasmic.

Embodiment practice – Whole-body freedom

I meet and observe so many women whose bodies look tense and rigid. I notice this with a woman on a dance floor or a client on the massage table and sometimes with my lover in my bed. When they move, the movements are mechanical, superficial or disjointed.

So, the main intention of this practice is to help you to move more freely. If you also feel sexual pleasure, then that's a bonus. But let the focus be to feel your body and the inherent pleasure in moving your body without inhibition.

1. Lie on your back on a semi-hard surface. Totally relax your body.
2. Now, start moving different parts of your body in isolation. Move your hips; make a wave motion through your spine; shake, tense and relax different muscles; open and close your hands, mouth and eyes; turn your shoulders, feet, hands, head and legs in circular movements; twist your spine; wiggle your fingers and toes; flare your nostrils; stretch your body; and make any other movements you can.
3. Gradually, move more and more parts of your body at the same time. Don't think about the movements. Rather, allow it to happen by itself. Notice what part of your body wants to move now and in what way it wants to move. Follow that impulse.
4. Find the pleasure in the movements. It doesn't have to be sexual pleasure; simply find the pleasure of moving your body in new ways.
5. Continue this for about ten minutes, then relax.

Witness the sensations in your body and note them in your orgasmic diary.

Learning to move all of your body in various ways without inhibition greatly helps you in your sexual and orgasmic awakening.

Embodiment practice – Gentle waves through your spine

When some women experience very strong orgasms, there is a physical wave of movement going up the spine. This can be a gentle or an intense kind of convulsion.

I've seen a few women who arch their back so much that it doesn't even touch the mattress – only their hips and the back of their head stays in contact with the mattress. They can stay in this position for long moments, shaking with pleasure and orgasmic energy. Let's explore the pleasure of moving your spine in this way:

1. Lie down on your back on a semi-hard surface with your knees raised. Don't put a pillow under your head.
2. Arch your back slightly, tilting your pelvis downwards towards your feet. Allow this movement to travel like a wave up your spine, causing your head to tilt backwards. Make sure you aren't doing this too intensely and hurting your back. If any pain appears, decrease the intensity or stop completely.
3. Relax your back and head then repeat this undulating movement for three to five minutes.
4. After this practice, notice any sensations or emotions you are experiencing. Write this down in your orgasmic diary.

Incorporate this way of moving into your self-pleasuring and love-making. This practice will allow you to experience the mild orgasmic state described earlier, and pave the way to longer and stronger orgasms. Once you are comfortable with this gentle movement, you are ready for some hip action.

Embodiment practice – Orgasmic hips

When we're talking about sexual movement, most of this comes from the hips. Your hips are closely connected to your sensuality as a woman. Think about belly dancers and how they move their hips or perhaps an erotic dancer. Hip movement is the core of any sensual dance. So, how can you move your hips to help embody more sensual and orgasmic energy?

This practice will take you through a series of movements to help you do this. Lie down on your back on a semi-hard surface, either naked or with loose cloths. Raise your knees. Then try out these movements:

1. Hip rolling (arch and tuck)

   - Imagine that your coccyx (tail-bone) is a small ball. Now roll that ball forwards and backwards on the mattress.

   - Another way to do this is to arch your back so your lower back lifts up from the mattress. Then tuck your pelvis so that your lower back is on the mattress and your buttocks are slightly raised above the mattress.

   - Do this back and forth movement for three to five minutes. Then relax and notice the effects.

2. Hip rolling with breath

   - Do the same back and forth movement as in step one but, this time, synchronize your breath with the movement.

   - Inhale when you arch your back. Exhale when you tuck your pelvis towards your chest and straighten your back. Notice that when you do this, your abdomen naturally compresses, pushing the air out effortlessly.

   - Do this for three to five minutes. Relax and notice the effects.

   Notice that if you get aroused, your breath can get out of sync with your movement. That's okay. If this happens, go into the intensity of the experience without worrying about syncing. Just make sure you are still moving *and* breathing.

3. Hip rolling with vaginal squeezes

   Once you get comfortable with the hip-rolling movement with breath, you can add another element – vaginal squeezes.

   - Inhale while arching your back.
   - Squeeze your vaginal muscles, exhale and tuck your pelvis.
   - Release the squeeze and inhale while arching again.
   - Continue this: Squeeze, exhale and tuck. Then release, inhale and arch.
   - Do this for three to five minutes. Relax and notice the effects. *(see Diagram 5 on page 152)*

Hip Rolling

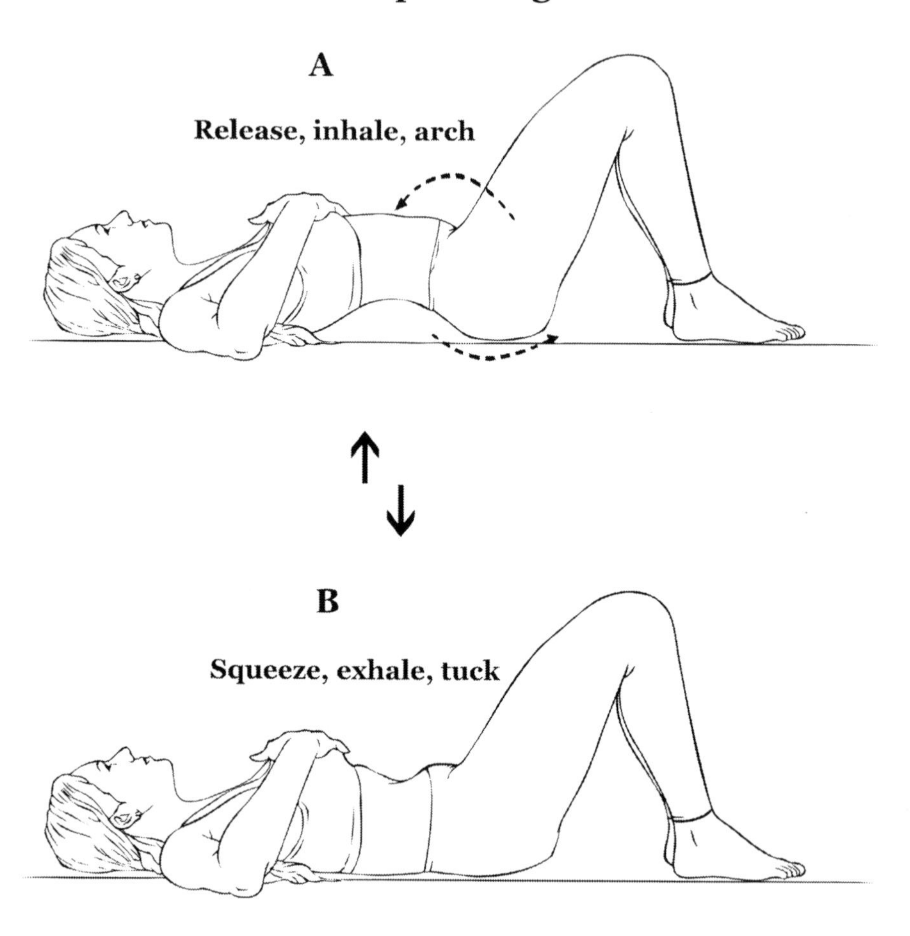

Diagram 5

If this is too complex, don't worry about it, and continue to the next exercise.

4. Hip circles

   - Make sure you breathe deeply into your lower belly while you do this movement.

- Move your hips in circles. Move them to the left, down and around to the right, then up and around to the left again.
- Then make these movements the other way around.
- Vary the speed and intensity of the movement. Experiment with small, gentle circles and then with larger, faster circles.
- Do this for three to five minutes. Relax and notice the effects.

5. Gentle hip bounces
   - Lift your hips from the mattress and gently bounce them up and down.
   - Start slowly and then gradually get faster and slightly stronger. Aim to reach around one to three bounces per second.
   - Do this for three to five minutes. Relax and notice the effects. *(see Diagram 6 on page 154)*

Hip Bounces

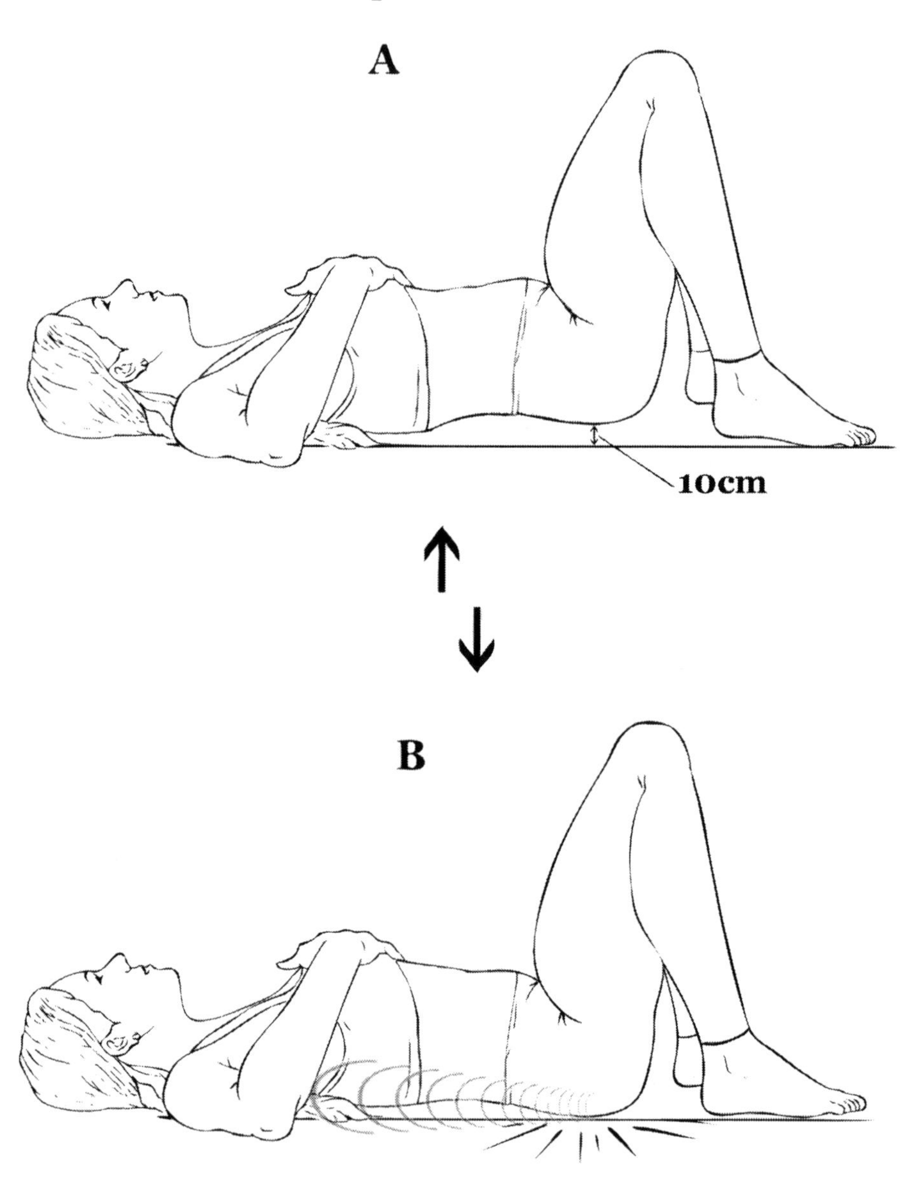

Diagram 6

6. Strong hip bounces
   - Make sure the surface or mattress is soft enough and be careful not to hurt your coccyx, sacrum or back in this practice!
   - Lift your hips high and then drop them strongly on the mattress.
   - Pause for a few seconds and notice the shock wave that goes up your spine. (Some women can go into a strong orgasm just from this technique alone.)
   - Do this for three to five minutes. Relax and notice the effects.
7. Putting it all together

   Once you have practiced all of the different hip movements, it's time to combine them. Take ten to fifteen minutes to explore the range of movement your hips can make. Be sure to keep breathing deeply into your belly and making loud sounds if you can. Then relax and notice the effects. Take time to describe all of your experiences in your orgasmic diary.

Incorporate these movements into your self-pleasuring practice, your love-making and also into your dance practice. When you can move your hips freely through a range of movements, you help intensify your orgasmic energy in this area and expand it throughout your body … and that often leads to orgasms!

Embodiment practice – Standing hip thrust

This is a very powerful practice that connects you to your sexuality, sensuality, power and wild side. When I facilitate it at my workshops, many people experience strong emotions, sensations, pleasure or even orgasms. And this is while they are standing up, fully clothed and in a room with other people.

If pain or dizziness appears, slow down or stop, taking care not to hurt yourself or faint. On the other hand, it's good to push it a bit beyond your comfort zone. That is where the magic happens.

1. Stand upright with your feet shoulder-width apart and your knees slightly bent. It's best if you are wearing loose clothes. You will probably get hot during this practice so wearing layers you can easily take off is perfect.

2. Arch your back and tilt your pelvis downwards. Then straighten your back and tuck your pelvis upwards. Make sure that the movement comes from tilting your hips and not just from moving them backwards and forwards. Bending your knees makes this easier.

   If a man knows what he's doing, this is the way he will penetrate you. Not jabbing back and forth, but more of a plunging up and in and then arching out. If it helps, imagine you are wearing a cock and thrusting your cock upwards while making love.

3. Once you get the movement going, you can add the breath. Exhale when you thrust forward, inhale when you arch your back. You might want to make the sound 'Ha' as you thrust because it helps synchronize the breath with the movement and to express the energy.

4. Continue this for eight to ten minutes, beginning with soft slow movements and progressing all the way to fast, hard and vigorous movements. Your breath and sound will go out of sync with your movement as you increase in intensity. That's okay. Just keep breathing deeply into your lower belly and making sounds as you move.

5. Relax, note the effects and write down your experience in your orgasmic diary

At the end of this practice, you may be able to feel your sexuality, sensuality and power moving through your body in a much stronger way. If you become comfortable with these feelings and expressions, they can help to expand and deepen your experience of orgasm.

Standing hip thrust

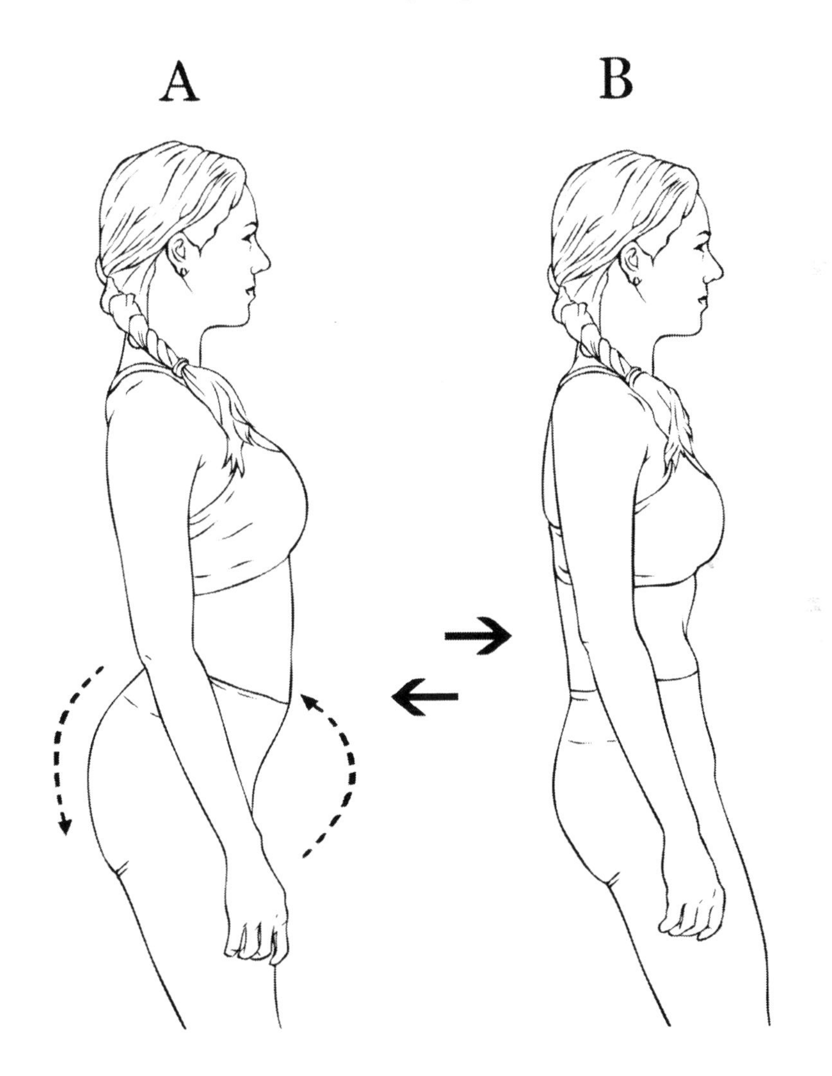

Diagram 7

Embodiment practice – Fucking the mattress

I guess the name of this practice says it all. I'm using the word 'fucking' very intentionally. This practice will connect you to the energy of fucking. There's great power in this word and in the practice of fucking. As a woman, it's important to embrace all aspects and energies of yourself and your sexuality.

This practice also connects you to your masculine side as well as the feminine aspect of being wild and out-of-control. You will experience your power and intensity, the energies of the first (root) and third (navel) chakras and the elements of earth and fire.

This practice will allow you to let go of guilt and shame around sexuality and experience more pleasure by yourself and with your partner through your uninhibited ability to move. It also allows you to express and let go of suppressed emotions. This practice might bring up memories or images of abuse or rape that want to be dealt with and healed.

So, as you are doing this, be aware of what comes up. Don't try to understand or analyze what is happening, just keep going. Using the combination of breath, sound, movement, fantasy, visualization and intention makes this a very powerful practice.

1. Lie on your front and perhaps put a large pillow under your hips.
2. Create an intention for your practice. It might be something like, 'Connect with my wild side' or 'Express my suppressed anger' or 'Heal my memories of being raped.'
3. Imagine you are a man and the pillow under you is a woman. Visualize what you look like and what the woman looks like. If you don't want to visualize yourself fucking a woman, you can visualize an aspect of yourself instead.

4. Start moving your hips as if you are inside her. Move your hips up and down, back and forth, side to side and in circles. Fuck her like you've always yearned to be fucked. Or do what you've fantasized about doing to someone else, a man or a woman.
5. Keep breathing deeply into your lower belly and making sounds. Talk to your lover. Tell her what you feel and what you want to do to her.
6. Gradually allow yourself to move faster, stronger and more vigorously. Allow yourself to really fuck her, take her and ravish her. You are serving this woman by sharing your powerful, wild, masculine energy with her.
7. Go even stronger, faster, wilder. Give her everything. EVERYTHING!
8. Allow yourself to express everything that comes up – movements, words, sounds, emotions.
9. Do this for ten to fifteen minutes if you can.
10. As I've mentioned earlier, male ejaculation is a habit that doesn't necessarily serve the man or his partner. But for the sake of this exercise, you can allow yourself to visualize and act out what a man does when he ejaculates if you wish.

When you decide you have finished, lie on your back and completely relax your body. Become aware of your sensations, feelings, thoughts and any insights you might have had while embracing this energy. Then write down your experiences in detail in your orgasmic diary. If stuff came up for you, you might want to do this again at a later time.

This is a great way to connect to your raw, wild, intense energy. This can help you bring more of this energy into your daily life in a way that serves both you and others.

Support your movement practice

One of my key messages to women is that sexual empowerment is achieved by yourself, with your partner and also by seeking the guidance of an experienced professional. Free movement is a great thing to practice both in the bedroom and in your daily life. Changing your daily life to support your sexual practice has great effects.

Here are a few things you can do to support your movement practice:

- Learn and then regularly practice the hula-hoop. This is a great way to feel, activate and unleash the pleasure and power of your hips. It's also great fun.
- Attend conscious dance evenings and workshops. Many clubs and parties are focused on getting drunk or high and talking to people with the intention of getting laid. At many conscious dance events, on the other hand, they don't serve alcohol, talking is discouraged and you dance with bare feet. People come to dance – alone and with others. They wear comfortable clothes that allow them to move. And while it's also a great place to flirt and hook up, it's not the main goal.
- Attend belly-dancing classes. Learn how to really move your hips, belly and breasts. Good teachers will also combine some aspects of femininity and sexuality into their teachings.
- Attend African dance or tribal dance classes. This is a great form of dance to connect to your hips, your root chakra and your wild side.
- Join erotic dance classes and workshops such as strip tease, pole dance or burlesque. These focus specifically on sensual and erotic movement and dance. While good, I usually prefer to recommend practices that are less structured and allow you to express your own unique erotic nature.

- Attend more formal or structured dance classes like samba, rumba, kisumba, tango, biodanza, and so on. Tango in particular is a very sensual dance that is related to both the second (sacral) and the third (navel) chakras – in other words – sexuality, power and control.

Orgasmic extras

To find conscious dance events, I recommend looking up: ecstatic dance, 5rhythms, contact dance, and movement medicine.

If you practice free-flowing movement in your everyday life, you will naturally move more freely when you are having sex. This freedom in movement expands how you experience orgasmic energy in your body and can bring great pleasure to your partner as well.

Position

The position your body is in while you are self-pleasuring or making love has several effects:

- It affects the flow of energy in your body. This is one of the secrets of yoga – every position has an effect on your chakras, energy flow and the kinds of energy that you experience. Some positions will charge your heart chakra while others will charge your sexual chakra.
- It has physiological effects owing to blood flow and the physical pressure on different body parts. For example, laying on your front puts pressure on your lower belly and pubic bone.
- It has psychological effects. Certain positions trigger thoughts and emotions. For example, if you are on all fours it might feel more animalistic and raw, while lying on your front might feel protected and safe.

Embodiment practice – Pleasure positions

As you are self-pleasuring and later during foreplay and love-making, experiment with some of the positions in this practice.

- Beginner's position

  Lie on your back with your legs straight and slightly open. This is a good position to begin with if you feel inhibited with other positions.

- Basic position

  Lie on your back with your feet on the mattress near your buttocks. Your knees should be pointing towards the ceiling, either slightly apart or wide apart. This position allows you to touch yourself easily, while moving your hips and the rest of your body.

Basic posisition

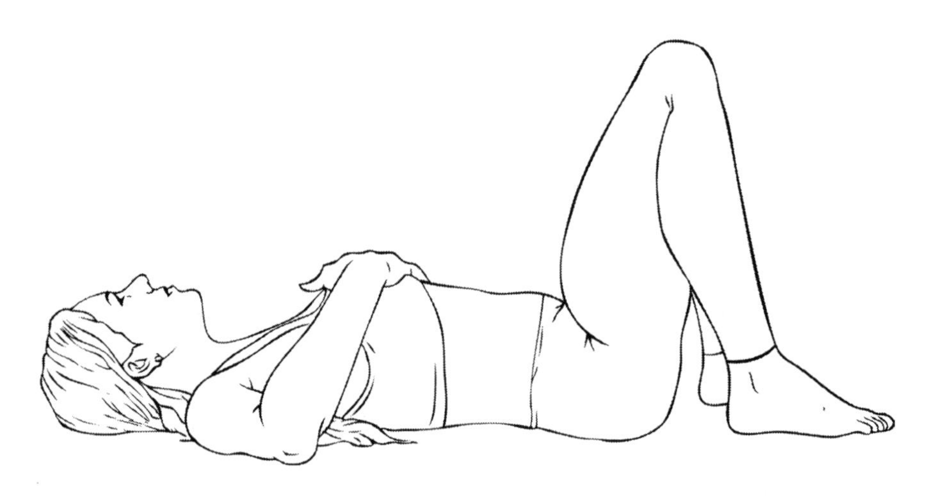

Diagram 8

- Open position

  Lie on your back with your feet pressed together and your knees wide apart. Your feet should be as close as possible to your buttocks and you can use pillows under your knees for support. This position opens your hip joints and your vagina. It has the psychological effect of feeling very open and also activates your first (root) and second (sacral) chakras.

Open posisition

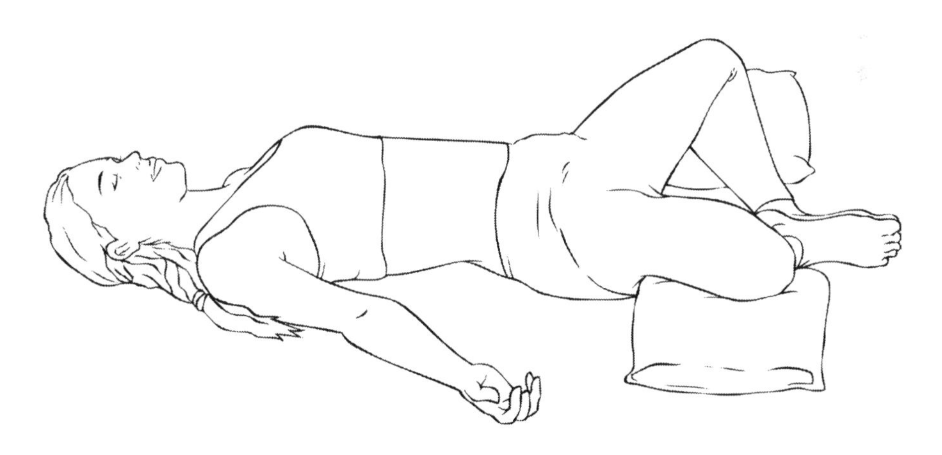

Diagram 9

Variations regarding your head position:

- Without a pillow under your head (recommended). This allows your body to move more easily and the energy to move more freely. It also opens the throat chakra.
- With a pillow under your shoulder blades. This opens the heart chakra and the throat chakra.

  - With a pillow under your head. This allows you to see your torso and lower body but might hinder your movements and energy flow. This is less recommended than the other two.

- Lying on your side

  You can use a thick pillow between your knees and a thin pillow under your head. This provides a feeling of safety, security and nurturing, although it doesn't allow for much movement.

- Lying on your front

  You can use one or even two hands to reach between your legs in this position. It activates your second chakra (sacral) and your yoni chakra, which is a secondary chakra related to sensuality and orgasmic energy.

- Sphinx pose

  Lying on your front, raise your head and chest and rest on your elbows. You can rub your pubic bone on the mattress and wiggle your legs. This doesn't allow for much movement but activates your sacral chakra, heart chakra and yoni chakra. It also stimulates the production of testosterone, which increases your libido.

- All fours or cat's pose

  Get on your hands and knees. This allows you to arch and tuck your spine very easily but doesn't allow you to touch yourself. As we explored earlier, arching and tucking your spine and pelvis activates your sexual energy and moves it around your body. You can use this position as a warm-up or if you are already aroused, you might be able to experience lots of pleasure in this position.

- Child's pose

  Sit on your shins and bend forwards. Curl up with your knees together and your chest and head leaning forward into the mattress. Your hands can be by your side or held behind your back.

This activates your heart chakra and allows energy to move from your lower chakras to your higher chakras. It brings a feeling of peace and interiorization. This position doesn't allow for much movement or stimulation but it's great to rest in after your self-love practice.

A variation of child's pose is with your knees apart. Sit on your knees and separate your knees and feet so they are as wide apart as possible. Then bend down so that your chest is on the mattress. You can touch yourself with one or two hands. This position opens your hips and activates your heart chakra. It can also help you to get accustomed to having a man enter you from behind.

- Standing position

  This promotes lucidity, confidence and awareness. It's easy to reach your yoni and move your spine at the same time. You can stand and masturbate in front of a mirror or a camera as an addition to this practice.

- Squatting position

  This opens your hip joints, activates the root chakra and makes it easier for you to reach deep inside your yoni. You probably won't be able to stay in this position for too long though.

- Sitting

  You can sit on the edge of a hard surface. This allows for easy stimulation of the front of the body and clitoris. It might be challenging to insert fingers, though, unless you slightly lean forward.

I recommend experimenting with these positions in a self-pleasuring session where you spend at least five minutes in each position. You don't have to try them all in the same session; about three to five different positions is a good start. Note the different effects of each in your orgasmic diary.

Once you have practiced with these positions, it will be easier for you to effortlessly incorporate them into your self-pleasuring and love-making. This allows you to enjoy the different effects that different positions have on your body, emotions and mental state. The next thing to explore is how different kinds of touch can improve your orgasmic experience.

Touch

Touch is one of the basic elements of sexuality and orgasm. The way you touch yourself and the way you are able to receive touch have huge influence on many things:

- How you feel.
- The sensations you have in your body.
- How much pleasure you are able to experience and contain.
- The different energies that are activated in your body.
- Your mental state.
- How many of the different kinds of orgasms you will be able to experience.

Self-reflection: *How do you touch yourself?*

Are you challenged by some kinds of touch? Does your lover touch you in one way but you yearn to be touched in a different way? Do you find it difficult to express how you want to be touched? All of these things can limit how you express your sexuality and experience pleasure and orgasm.

Over many years as a sexuality coach, I've noticed that people generally become used to touch in one specific way or in a very few specific ways. They find giving and receiving touch in other ways either boring or challenging. For example, some women enjoy soft touch and a very particular kind of soft touch, and they don't like hard touch at all. Others need hard touch in order to feel pleasure and can't feel anything if they are touched softly.

I once worked with a woman who couldn't orgasm at all. The sexual energy would immediately shoot up to her upper body and she would hardly feel any physical pleasure in her genitals and lower body. She was a very intense, determined and even slightly harsh person. She was driven and goal-oriented but lacked softness and sweetness.

During one of our sessions, I was stimulating her yoni and no matter how hard or fast I went, it wasn't strong enough for her. My hands were getting tired but she could hardly feel anything. Then I changed the touch. I slowed down and touched her yoni very lightly. She said, 'I can't feel you. I can't feel anything at all.' But I kept going softly for a few minutes. She kept saying she couldn't feel anything and asked me to please go harder. Still, I kept the soft, light touch. Then suddenly she said, 'I just had an orgasm.' It wasn't a mind-blowing or earth-shattering orgasm, but it was definitely an orgasm. It was one of the first internal orgasms she had experienced, and a very special one.

In this example, I learned the important of softness and subtlety. And later, I realized that while that woman had a lot of navel chakra energy, what she actually needed was a combination of the softness of the heart chakra and the sensuality of the sacral chakra. She ended up spending the next few years practicing yoga and living in a tantric community. She developed her feminine side – sweet, soft and innocent – but she also kept her sharp mind, intensity and determination.

This was a valuable lesson for me. I learned that people don't always know what touch they need and that sometimes they need to be given something that they don't usually go for. So this learning inspired me to create a powerful practice that can help you to experience and embrace the energies of different touch. We'll get to that shortly. First, let's start with practice to embody sensual touch.

Embodiment practice – Whole-body sensual touch

This practice brings sensual touch to your whole body without involving your genitals. This will show you that you can experience pleasure without even touching your genitals.

1. Sit or lie down comfortably.
2. Caress your whole body, excluding your genitals, for about five minutes in whatever way you feel like. Don't worry about it being sensual or sexual, just bring touch and sensation to your whole body.
3. Then try different kinds of touch. Spend a few minutes exploring touch that is:
   - Light and airy. For example, try blowing air on your skin. Try it again after licking your skin.
   - Strong and earthy. For example, try pressing hard into your flesh; feel your bones.
   - Flowing and watery. For example, try continuous caresses in circular movements.
   - Intense and fiery. For example try pulling at your skin or scratching.
4. Spend at least ten to fifteen minutes exploring the different sensations throughout your body.
5. Use heart-shaped hand movements. To experience whole-body orgasms or at least whole-body pleasure, you can try spreading the orgasmic energy from your genitals towards your upper

body. Move both of your hands from your genitals, up through the middle of your belly, to your belly button, then spread your hands to the sides of your body and go back down to your genitals. Notice that this creates a kind of heart shape on your body. Then go up to your lower ribs and back down your sides. Then go up until the middle of your chest. Then up to your throat. The exact location isn't important. The idea is to move both your hands in bigger and bigger heart shapes up and over your body, and then start again from your lower belly.

6. Relax and note how you are feeling. Write down your experiences in your orgasmic diary.

I recommend you spend time touching your whole body for a few minutes every single day – preferably in the morning. This practice is a very simple way to bring sensation and awareness to your entire body, and is a great preparation for the next practice.

Embodiment practice – Five elements tantric touch

As a long-time yoga student and practitioner, I have come to realize that different kinds of touch are related to different chakras and to the five elements – earth, water, fire, air and ether.

I've developed this practice to help others give and receive various kinds of touch according to the five elements. I usually facilitate this practice at my workshops as a couple's practice but you can still get a lot out of it by doing it yourself. You can always get a feel for it and then share it with your partner later.

The benefits of this practice include being able to give and receive new kinds of touch, experiencing new kinds of pleasure, healing from sexual pain and trauma, experiencing variety and novelty, and potentially opening up to more kinds of orgasm.

What you need to do is touch yourself according to the energy of the five elements. Do this one at a time and spend about two to five minutes on each. The five elements are described below:

- Air

  The air touch is related to the heart chakra and the aspects of love and a very refined sensuality. It is airy, fairy and light. Try using the tips of your fingers, touching-not-touching, making very light contact with the surface of your skin. You can also blow air across your skin, and perhaps use your hair or a light piece of material to caress yourself.

- Water

  The water touch is related to the sacral chakra and embodies sensuality and nurturing. It is long, slow, circular and flowing movements. Try touching your skin using the entire surface of your hand but without applying pressure. Imagine you have oil in your hand and that you're rubbing it all over your skin.

- Earth

  The earth touch is related to the root chakra and is a combination of rawness and stability. This touch connects to the deep flesh and the bones. It is a slow, gradual and deliberate touch. Try pressing and pushing into your body using a large surface area of your hands or arms. You make contact, push in gradually, go to the strongest pressure you can apply, hold it for a while and then release gradually. You can also grab your fleshy areas such as your belly, waist, thighs and buttocks.

- Fire

  The fire touch is related to the navel chakra. This touch is fast, intense, sharp and constantly changing. You can try scratching, biting, pinching, pulling, slapping and smacking yourself. This touch builds energy very rapidly and can bring up resistance or judgment in those that aren't used to it. On the contrary, you might find it very amusing and start giggling and laughing.

- Ether

  Related to the throat chakra, the ether touch is not touching at all. Rather, try moving your hands above your body. This touch works on the energetic or 'etheric' level. Start by rubbing your hands against each other for a minute and than bring them closer and closer to your body until you feel a slight tingling or different sensation in your hands. This is where your hands meet the energetic field of your body. Imagine your hands are touching your energy field. Move this energy around, circulate it or draw it outwards as if you are pulling a string. You can also imagine that your hands are emanating heat, similar to superman. Yes, you can have super powers too!

After you have spent a few minutes with each element, notice if one of the elements is challenging, triggering or boring for you. Then, you guessed it, try to explore this particular element further. Write down your experiences in your orgasmic diary.

After you've explored each of the different elements separately, take some time for free-form play that incorporates sensual touch, self-pleasure and the five elements. Write down what you experience in your orgasmic diary.

Also consider doing a couple's practice of the five elements with your partner or even with a close friend. It doesn't have to be sexual. Each person expresses the touch of the five elements on their partner's body in the same way as described above. This can take fifteen to forty-five minutes in total. After one person has given touch for all five elements, switch.

Although it might seem simple, this is actually one of the most effective practices in this book. Learning to integrate different kinds of touch with your sexuality will bring new energies and sensations to your sex life as well as to other aspects of your life. For example, if you don't like the fiery touch, you might have an issue connected with the navel chakra, which can be related to self-confidence and taking action. When you develop greater comfort with the different touches, you can empower yourself in areas of your life that you have been previously challenged by.

Pussy power

To orgasm for the first time or to improve your orgasmic experience, it's important that you can feel what's going on inside you. You want your yoni to be sensitive to different kinds of touch. And vaginal fitness can make a real difference to your pussy power. This connects to the pleasure you are able to feel and the strength of the orgasms you can have.

Self-reflection: *How well can you feel your muscles down there? Squeeze your vaginal muscles to get a sense of this.*

Techniques for strengthening the vaginal muscles have been taught and practiced in both the Indian Tantric and Chinese Taoist traditions as well as in tribal cultures in some parts of the world. These days, these practices are known as 'kegel exercises' and might be referred to as pelvic floor or PC muscle exercises (called this because they relate to the pubococcygeus muscle).

There are many benefits of exercising and strengthening your vaginal muscles. Here are just a few:

- It promotes vaginal health and reduces the risk of illnesses in sexual and reproductive organs.
- It reduces the severity of urinary incontinence and can even solve the condition.

- It connects you to your yoni, your body and your femininity.
- It makes it easier to turn clitoral stimulation into internal orgasm.
- It enhances pleasure and makes it easier to experience internal orgasms, whole-body orgasms and orgasmic states.
- It can facilitate the experience of female ejaculation.
- It helps you to move energy up your spine and to your higher chakras.
- It facilitates pleasure for your partner and in advanced levels of practice, makes it possible to delay a man's ejaculation.
- It is great preparation for childbirth and a recovery practice afterwards.

So, building up your pussy power with vaginal fitness is worth thinking about and exploring if you are serious about your orgasmic practice and your health.

Embodiment practice – Feel your pussy power

This practice will help you to perceive the strength of your yoni muscles. As you are reading, become aware of your yoni. Notice how well can you feel her.

1. Get yourself aroused and naturally lubricated using some of the practices we explored earlier in the book.
2. Put one finger inside your yoni. How well can you feel the place or area where your finger is touching the inside of your yoni?
3. Insert two fingers into your yoni. Then spread your fingers apart.
4. Squeeze your vaginal muscles and feel the pressure on your fingers. If you are unsure of which muscles to squeeze, you can identify

it easily the next time you go to the bathroom. When you are midway through peeing – stop. The muscle that stops the flow is your PC muscle. Don't do this (stopping your flow of urine) on a regular basis, as it might cause a UTI (Urinary Tract Infection). You only need to do this if you are unsure about which muscle to squeeze.

5. Notice the strength of your muscles at this point in time.

If you choose to build your pussy power with vaginal strengthening exercises, I recommend doing this practice every week or so. You will notice that your muscles are gradually becoming stronger and, at the same time, how your pleasure has deepened and expanded.

Embodiment practice – Vaginal workout

As I mentioned earlier, strengthening your vaginal muscles has many effects, including more pleasure, new kinds of orgasm and genital health. The exercises in this practice will help with this.

Before you start working on your muscles, it's important to make sure that they are relaxed and not tensed. The first time you try these exercises, I recommend starting with a short self-pleasuring practice. Then, when you feel you're ready, you can start experimenting with the different exercises. After your first time, you can practice them daily without having a warm-up.

You might want to put two fingers inside as explained in the previous exercise so you can feel the difference between the different squeezes on your own fingers.

- Squeeze – This is the most basic vaginal fitness exercise, and one that most women will probably find easy to do. Simply squeeze your vagina as explained in the previous practice. There are a few variations to how you can practice your vaginal squeezes, with each producing a slightly different effect:

- Fast – Squeeze, release, squeeze, release.
- Slow – Squeeze, hold the squeeze for one to two seconds, release. Squeeze-hold-release.
- Continuous – Squeeze and hold for as long as you can. After a while, you will notice that your muscles have naturally relaxed. Squeeze again and hold as long as you can.

Start with twenty fast squeezes, ten slow squeezes and five continuous ones (or about two minutes of continuous squeezes). You can do less if you get tired or more if it's too easy for you. Gradually increase by a few repetitions every day.

Vaginal workout - Squeeze

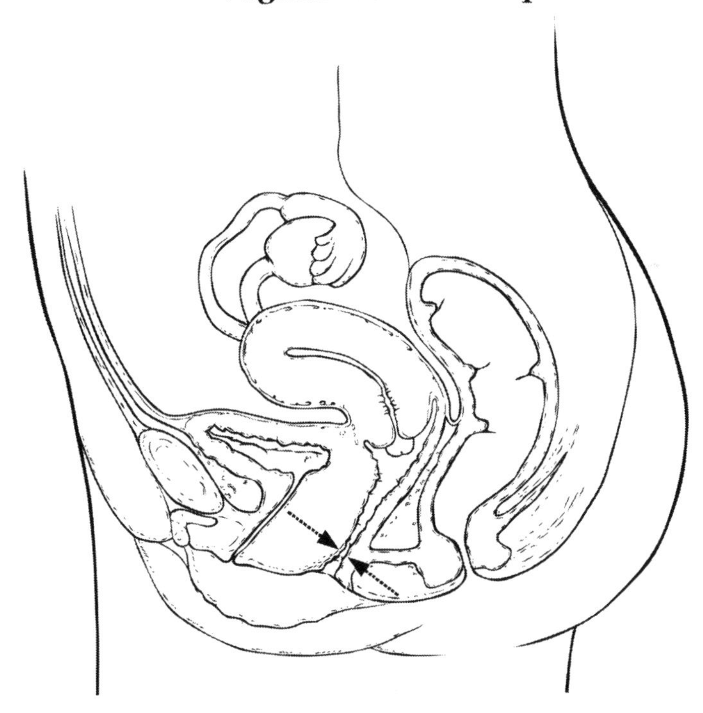

Diagram 10

- Deep squeeze – Some women can squeeze the deep part of their vagina, in the area of their cervix. Very few women can do this, but it's good to know that it is possible to learn.

Vaginal workout - Deep squeeze

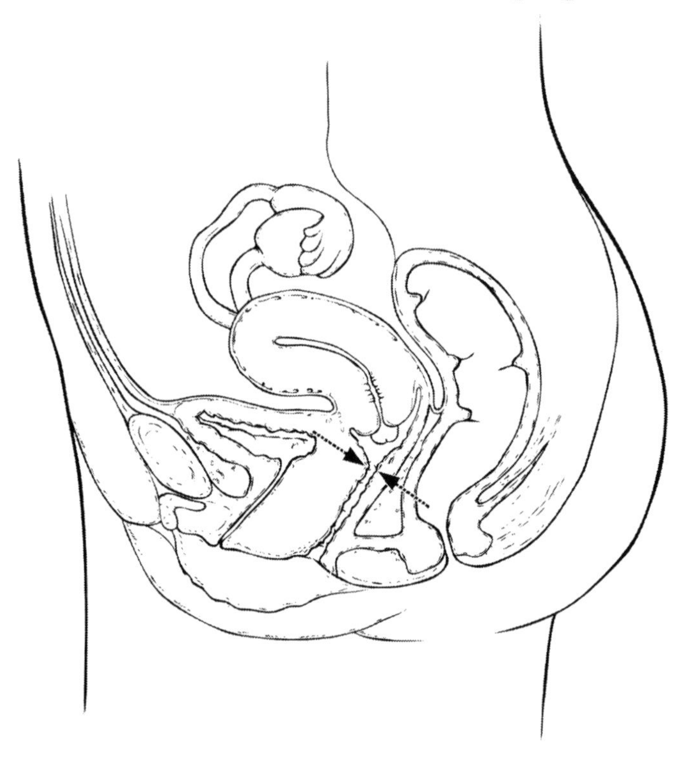

Diagram 11

- Push – Imagine that you have something inside your yoni, like a tampon, and that you are pushing your muscles out in order to expel it. Some women can push their muscles out so much that some of the inner surface of their yoni comes out and their G-spot becomes visible. *(see Diagram 12 on page 177)*

Vaginal workout - Push

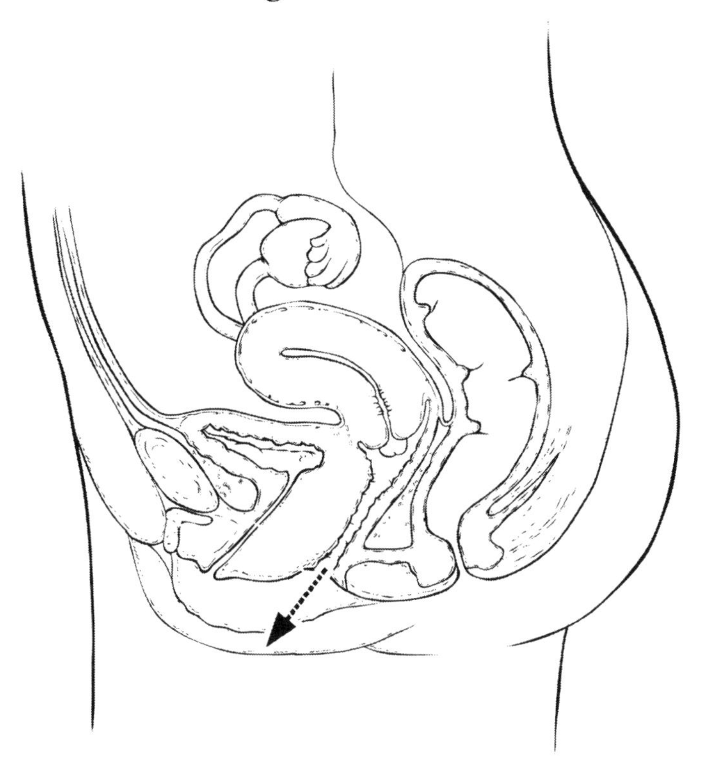

Diagram 12

- Pull – Imagine that you are trying to draw your man's cock into you, or that there's a string that is connected from your cervix to his cock. Now squeeze your vagina while pulling inwards. *(see Diagram 13 on page 178)*

Vaginal workout - Pull

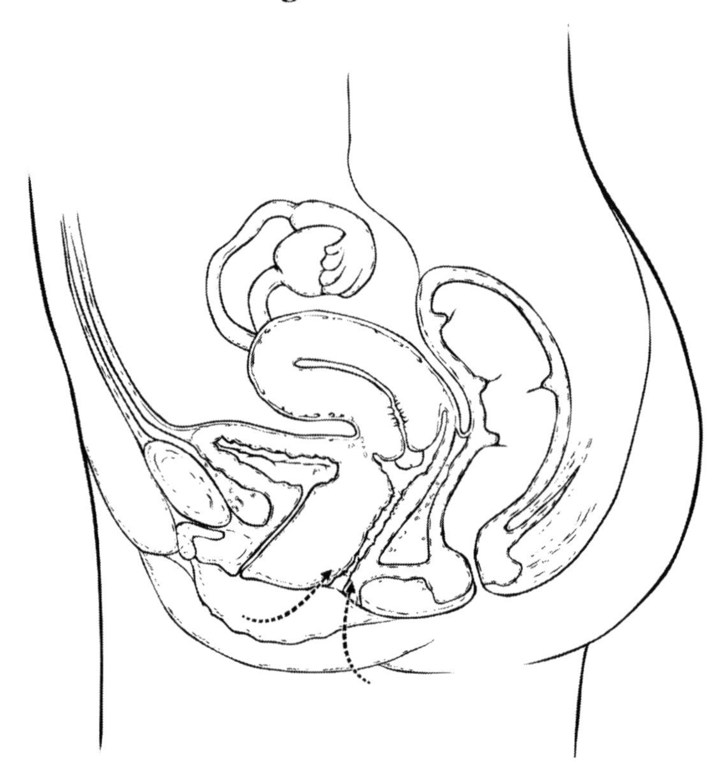

Diagram 13

- Push-pull – Alternating between pushing and pulling.

Much like the basic squeeze, you could do repetitions of the other kinds of vaginal exercises as a part of your practice, such as the push and the pull. Commit to doing vaginal exercises every day and on every occasion you have time, such as in traffic jams and boring meetings. Rather than seeing this as homework or a duty, know that it is a simple way to feel and connect to your yoni wherever you are.

If you have a partner, you can do some of these exercises while you're making love and notice the effects. As a man, it feels like my partner is kissing me with her yoni when she is squeezing. It feels amazing!

However, even though these exercises are great for both pleasure and health, make sure that you also allow yourself to completely relax your muscles as you self-pleasure or have sex. This goes for all techniques and practices that we've explored. Practice them and experiment with them, but also allow yourself to completely drop them from time to time, and simply explore sex and pleasure without trying to do anything.

Gradually, the activation of your yoni muscles will become automatic and you won't have to think about it. These exercises will help you to have more sensation in your yoni, experience more pleasure and orgasm, and can even affect other aspects of your life such as your physical and emotional health. Due to its many benefits, this is an important practice. So make sure you dedicate the time and attention for it every day, and witness how your pleasure and orgasm are unleashed in mind-blowing experiences!

How jade eggs can help

One of the best ways to practice and strengthen your vaginal muscles is to use a yoni egg or a jade egg. I highly recommend using eggs that are made of pure jade because this has a neutral effect on your yoni. Stay away from crystal or other materials.

Jade eggs are egg-shaped pieces of pure jade that you insert into your yoni and can move around with your muscles. Your egg should have a hole drilled through it so you can attach a piece of string and pull it out easily. Your jade egg should come with a booklet or a video that explains how to care for it and the different exercises and practices you can do with it.

You could also wear a jade egg throughout the day – just make sure that you wear underwear though. Otherwise, if you laugh or cough, you might accidentally 'lay an egg' and have it roll away on the floor. This actually happened to my partner once!

After a few weeks of basic jade egg practice, you can begin more advanced exercises where you attach a small weight to your egg and then squeeze your muscles so strongly that the egg stays in place. You can even try to pull the egg deeper into your body with your muscles so that you lift the weight. 'Look ma! No hands!' This is truly vaginal weightlifting. Believe it or not, there are world records for the heaviest weight a woman can hold with her vaginal muscles.

Wearing your jade egg and doing the recommended practices daily can complement or even replace the vaginal fitness exercises we explored earlier. Aside from vaginal exercises and jade egg practices, you could also attend Pilates or Vinyasa flow classes, given that they place a lot of emphasis on your pelvic floor muscles.

When you set out to increase your pussy power with these practices, you will soon notice a deeper connection with your yoni, more pleasure throughout your body, new kinds of orgasm and a deeper sense of personal power, as well as feeling more feminine and sensual. The importance of connecting with your vagina is central to your orgasmic experience.

Orgasmic extras

Check out the online resources section of my website for my recommendation about where to get your jade egg and a helpful DVD guide (www.intimatepower.com/orgasm-book-resources).

You orgasmic power is ever increasing

The techniques that have been shared in this section can really power up your orgasms – the best thing you can do is try them out and see what works for you. When you incorporate breath, sound, movement, position and touch into your sexual expression, you become more and more orgasmic. Vaginal fitness makes a significant difference too. From this point, a whole new world of orgasm awaits you.

6

Unleash your orgasm

So far we have explored the major kinds of orgasm, and various ideas and practices that help make it possible for you to expand your pleasure and subsequently experience more from your sex life – both with yourself and with your partner. These are essential, the building blocks, and the more you practice them, the more you will get out of your orgasmic experience and your sex life. Before we continue, it's a good idea to check in with how your orgasmic journey is unfolding.

Self-reflection: *How is your daily self-pleasuring practice progressing? Have you been able to focus on internal stimulation? What has come up for you? How has your experience of pleasure and orgasm changed? What effects have you noticed in other areas of your life?*

If you haven't started a daily practice yet, it's important that you decide to invest in yourself and make the commitment to do this every single day for at least one month. Consider revisiting the 'self pleasure tapas' to remind yourself of the many benefits available to you.

If you have been doing a daily self-pleasuring practice, you might already be experiencing some new kinds of orgasms. At the beginning of this book, we discussed the orgasm landscape – explosive clitoral orgasms with short and sharp peaks and implosive vaginal orgasms with longer, more expansive states. Then we explored the importance of appreciating all sensation of pleasure as a mini orgasm. Remember that you can still enjoy clitoral stimulation as part of your self-pleasuring. It's a great way to expand your pleasure. Just make sure you don't 'explode' your orgasm outwards; instead, draw it inwards and upwards so you can spread it around your body.

Often, an orgasm will feel like a combination of different kinds of orgasms. Once you have awakened your ability to experience a vaginal orgasm, you will likely experience a blended orgasm. A common blended orgasm is one that arises from the simultaneous stimulation of the clitoris and the vagina internally. Because the clitoris is adjacent to the entrance of the vagina, most kinds of vaginal stimulation and penetration will also stimulate the clitoris.

A blended orgasm combines the sensations of a peak orgasm and a whole-body orgasm. The experience and sensations of this orgasm can be felt as centered in and emanating from the genitals as well as being felt throughout your whole body. Imagine that – your whole body orgasming! Maybe you have experienced this already? And if not, the practices in this book will definitely make this a possibility for you.

But your orgasmic potential does not stop here; there are many, many ways orgasm can be experienced in your body and it does not always have to be centered in your genital area. Another way to look at orgasms is according to where in the body they stem from or are felt.

Now it's time to really unleash your orgasm! In this section, we're going to explore many different and exciting kinds of pleasure sensations, sexual experiences and – oh yes! – orgasms. You will learn special practices that will allow you to expand your orgasms so they are stronger, deeper, longer and more meaningful than ever.

Are you ready to unleash your orgasm?

Erogenous orgasm zones

You can differentiate between different kinds of orgasm according to the area that is being stimulated and aroused. We've already covered the clitoral orgasm and the vaginal orgasm in depth. But an orgasm can originate from prolonged stimulation of many different areas in your body. Sometimes these areas are related to an energy center or chakra that can affect your experience of a particular orgasm. We'll be covering the energetic centers in a bit more detail shortly. For now, let's first look at some of these orgasmic erogenous zones.

Vaginal entrance orgasm

There are many nerves at the entrance of your vagina, making it a sensitive and erogenous zone. Apart from the clitoral orgasm, this is the area where most women experience pleasure and subsequent orgasm. This orgasm is related to the root chakra, which is located at or near the perineum. It may feel earthy, raw and intense.

If a man is penetrating you shallowly and stimulating your vaginal entrance, it can feel very pleasurable on a physical level, but notice that when he enters you more deeply, the pleasure experience can become deeper, more expansive and even more meaningful. So, I guess size does matter as well as depth. Compared with more internal orgasmic areas, the vaginal entrance orgasm is shallower and sharper, similar to a clitoral orgasm and might also be explosive.

G-spot orgasm

We've all heard of the G-spot, originally called the Grafenberg spot after the scientist who 'discovered' it. How unsexy! So I prefer to think of it as the 'Goddess spot' or the 'Good spot.'

The G-spot is not actually an exact spot but more of an area located close to the entrance of the vagina, on the upper wall under the pubic bone. If you insert your index and middle fingers into your vagina and curl or hook them towards your clit, you will find an area that feels different to your vaginal walls. It's like a ridged and soft fleshy hill that feels like something between a hard tongue and a soft palate. All women have a G-spot. Some are located closer to the vaginal entrance while others are a bit deeper inside.

Your G-spot becomes much more engorged and swollen when you are aroused. A G-spot orgasm will be experienced as intense or even overwhelming pleasure. It is not as sharp as a clitoral orgasm, but more round and expansive. There will be strong contractions of your whole pelvic floor, including your PC muscles and vaginal muscles. Sometimes there is an expulsion of fluids from the vagina or urethra, also known as female ejaculation.

A G-spot orgasm will be more emotionally intense and meaningful, often followed by a feeling of deep satisfaction and relaxation. The pleasure subsides slowly and gradually. Subsequent orgasms can be easily experienced if arousal of the G-spot continues and this kind of orgasm can easily turn into an intense orgasmic state, lasting for many minutes or even hours.

Cervical-uterine orgasm

A cervical orgasm, for many women, is the most profound, meaningful and special orgasm that can be experienced, at least on the physical level.

The cervix is the entrance to the womb and in some ways it is the center of the feminine energies in a woman's body (or her primary polarity point). A woman's cervix is intimately connected to her sense of self, her heart, her creativity and her entire being.

A cervical orgasm is characterized by contractions of the deep vaginal muscles and uterus, while the PC muscle may stay relaxed. This orgasm will feel even deeper, more intense and more rounded than the G-spot orgasm. It is also usually accompanied by strong emotions or feelings of love, ecstasy, transcendence and perhaps tears. Many women describe a feeling of deep satisfaction on all levels along with a sense of oneness with themself, their partner and God.

According to the Tantric tradition, this is the most beneficial orgasm because it moves the sexual energy towards the higher chakras. It is related to the navel chakra (Manipura chakra) but the energy easily rises up to the heart chakra and beyond.

The experience of physical pleasure is deep and profound, but at the same time, the cervical orgasm is experienced and appreciated as something that is beyond bodily pleasure.

Nipple orgasm

Nipples are an important erogenous zone. Your nipples are connected via energy channels to your clitoris, therefore, stimulation of your breasts can cause arousal of your clitoris and your whole genital area.

Continued stimulation of the breasts and nipples can result in an orgasm or can bring about a genital orgasm more quickly and easily when vaginal stimulation is also applied. If your breasts are not very sensitive, you can increase the sensations you experience by giving yourself regular breast massages for at least twenty minutes a day as discussed in an earlier practice. Or, you can ask your partner to do this for you, if you have one.

Urinary orgasm

A urinary orgasm is a less common kind of orgasm. A woman who is sexually aroused might urinate while having an orgasm. This orgasm stems from the build up of sexual energy in your second chakra, and is more likely to occur when your bladder is full. Some people actually like having sex when their bladder is full because of this sensation.

In other cases, you might experience this type of orgasm when you urinate. If you were aroused but didn't orgasm, you may still be charged with this strong sexual energy. Then when you go to the toilet to urinate, you need to relax in order to 'shift gears' to enable urination. This relaxation together with the sexual energy might cause some women to have an orgasm, or at least a pleasure wave going up their spine.

A urinary orgasm can feel good and relieving, but it is much less pleasurable and satisfying compared with a G-spot or cervical orgasm, for example.

Anal orgasm

The anus is yet another erogenous zone, full of sensitive nerves. Some women are more open to anal stimulation than others and some will experience greater sensation and pleasure in this area. A small percentage of women (about five to ten per cent) need to have frequent anal stimulation or anal sex so as to feel satisfied. Otherwise they feel heavy, stagnant and stuck energetically.

An anal orgasm will generally be localized in the genital area. It's related to the root chakra so it will be earthy, raw, rough and physical. This kind of orgasm can be explosive, and if your partner is trying to avoid ejaculation, he should take extra care when penetrating you anally because it can be more challenging to control his ejaculation.

Throat orgasm

Some women can orgasm when performing fellatio, especially when deep throating. This orgasm can also stem from having a finger or two rubbing the back of the throat. These orgasms are related to the pituitary gland that is close to this area and is also a minor chakra, according to Tantra.

A throat orgasm feels pleasurable. It is accompanied by convulsions and spasms and the need to make strong sounds. Some women need to pause if they are giving head because the orgasm is so strong they can't continue. The effects of this orgasm are similar to the physiological effects of holding your breath and the suppression of the gag reflex. Some women excrete huge quantities of saliva and mucus that can be quite viscous in texture. Sometimes there is even a sort of white foam that is expelled from the mouth. The release of these fluids is considered to be a throat ejaculation.

Frequent stimulation of the throat and experiencing this type of orgasm can cause the opening of a woman's creative and artistic abilities, the expression of her needs and her higher potential. A throat orgasm can also help you sublime or channel the strong sexual energies from your lower chakras into a more refined energy in your higher chakras. In other words, it can shift you from horny and restless to relaxed and focused. Although very pleasurable, a throat orgasm feels more transcendent. Some women go into a semi-trance state and say they experience a higher and more pure state of consciousness.

My partner once couldn't sleep after we made love because she was so charged with energy. She tried different yogic techniques for about half an hour but couldn't move the energy away from her genitals. She then took me in her mouth, resulting in a massive throat orgasm with strong body convulsions. Her energy shifted almost immediately. She fell asleep soon after.

Orgasmic extras

If you ever feel so horny that you can't sleep and it's driving you crazy, check out the article "Horny? Can't sleep? Try this" on my online resources section on my website (www.intimatepower.com/orgasm-book-resources). You'll find ideas and practices on how to move this energy.

Female Anatomy

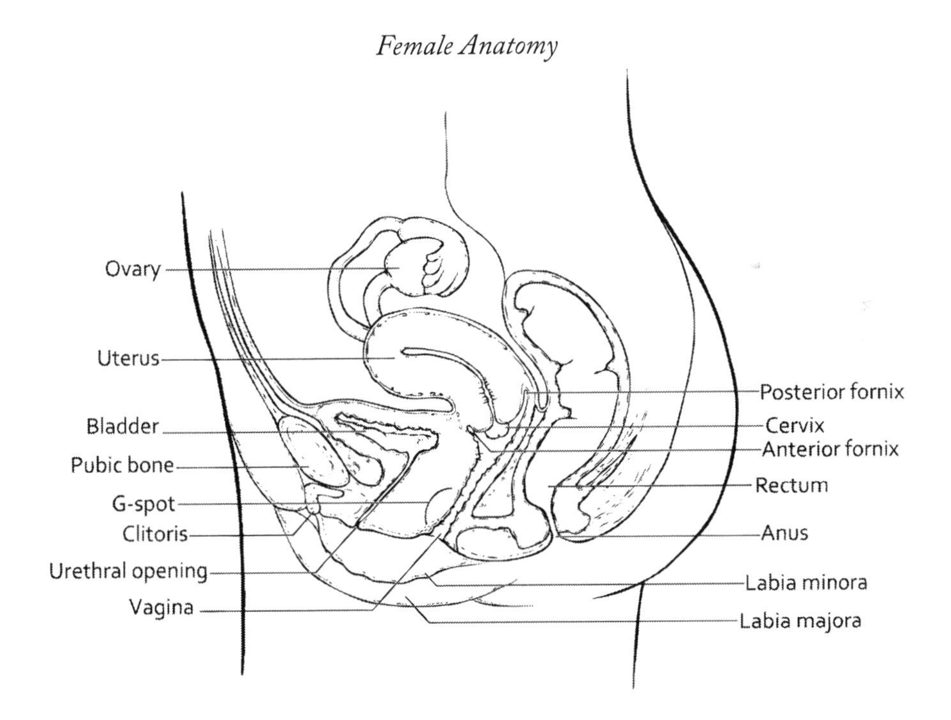

Diagram 14

Other orgasm hot spots

There are other specific areas in your body that can produce very distinct experiences of pleasure and orgasm. These are usually located in particular spots, much like the G-spot. Let's see what other hot spots are waiting to be discovered.

A-spot orgasm

The Anterior Fornix Erogenous (AFE) is more conveniently called the A-spot. This area is located on the upper wall of the vagina, further away from the G-spot and closer to the cervix. Again, it's not really a spot but an area about the size of a coin. I like to call this the 'Awesome-spot.'

Pleasure and orgasm that come from the stimulation of this area is experienced as something between the intense pleasure of the G-spot and the more emotional, transcendent pleasure of the cervix. Sometimes, stimulation can feel like the need to urinate because pressure is applied to the bladder. Daily stimulation of your A-spot can increase your vaginal lubrication.

PF-spot orgasm

The Posterior Fornix Erogenous (PFE) is located beneath the cervix on the back of the wall of the vagina, which is next to the rectum. Some sexual educators call this area the 'P-spot' but because this term is also used for the male prostate, I prefer to call it the PF-spot.

Stimulating the PF-spot is anal for people who don't like anal. This is like beginner's anal because it feels like anal stimulation without any anal penetration or contact with fecal material. It is great preparation if you are interested in exploring *actual* anal stimulation or anal sex.

The pleasure and orgasm derived from this area is often experienced as a combination of raw anal pleasure and expansive, emotional, spiritual cervical pleasure.

U-spot orgasm

The U-spot is located under the clit and surrounds the urethral opening in a kind of reverse 'U' shape. An orgasm in this area is related to the clitoral orgasm and might be explosive in nature.

K-spot orgasm

The K-spot is located at the coccyx, or the base of the spine, just above the anus. The K-spot is the kundalini spot and takes a while to arouse. However, an orgasm in this area can produce a very special experience of pleasure. It often causes electric waves of pleasure and other sensations to shoot up the spine.

Chakra orgasms

Chakras are energy points in the subtle body, not the physical body. According to the Tantric texts, there are many secondary chakras in the human body, but there are seven chakras that are considered to be the most important ones. The chakras are actually located outside of the physical body, but for ease we refer to them as being 'at the level' of a certain body part.

Generally speaking, sexual energy comes from the two lower chakras – Muladhara (root) and Svadistana (sacral). Chakra orgasms can unfold from the stimulation of the area related to the chakra, for example, stimulation of the chest and breasts can cause a heart-chakra orgasm. But chakra orgasms can also come from the build up of sexual energy when you don't lose your energy via an explosive orgasm. When you build sexual stimulation, pleasure and energy, the orgasms can start on one of the lower chakras, usually the second chakra, and either stay there or move progressively to higher and higher chakras. This often depends on the energy of both partners, their mental focus, the position they choose, the way they make love (for example, slow and gentle, hard and fast, shallow or deep penetration) and various other factors.

When you experience an orgasm at the level of a certain chakra, it will feel different to an orgasm via another chakra. The main characteristics of how each chakra affects your experience of an orgasm are described below:

- Muladhara or root chakra

  Located at the base of the spine and experienced as intense, earthy, rough, raw or physical.

- Svadistana or sacral chakra

  Located half way between the navel and the clit – most women have some experience of this one – it feels sexual, sensual, kinky and watery. This is what most people consider 'sexual' pleasure.

- Manipura or navel chakra

  Located at the navel and experienced as fiery, hot and intense. You might be instantaneously drenched in sweat and feeling like you are melting from the heat. Strangely enough, it can also lead to uncontrollable laughter.

- Anahata or heart chakra

  Located at the middle of the chest and experienced as an overwhelming feeling of love and unity with the partner and with life. The pleasure feels secondary to the feeling of love. Often you will cry, not out of sadness but as an expression of the profundity of the experience.

- Vishudha or throat chakra

  Located at the level of the pit of the throat and experienced as an altered perception of time and space. It feels refined, sublimed and pure.

- Ajna or third-eye chakra

  Located between the eyes in the center of the forehead and experienced as laser-like mental clarity and focus. It feels like pure presence and awareness, a balance of masculine and feminine energies and a feeling of 'knowing' yourself.

- Sahasrara or crown chakra

  Located above the top of the head and experienced as a diminished or loss of identification with the personal 'self' or the physical body, unity with the divine, dissolution, complete surrender, higher state of consciousness. It is characterized by very slow and shallow breath or even a stopping of the breath.

As you are self-pleasuring or making love, notice if your experience resonates with any of the descriptions above, but don't get too attached to these definitions or states. These orgasms can come from touching the body or from *not* touching the body.

Energy orgasms

Energy orgasm is a general name for many kinds of orgasm that do not involve genital touch or any touch at all. They can be experienced by yourself or with another person, with or without your clothes, and in either sexual or non-sexual situations.

There are sexual healers who facilitate different orgasmic states for their clients with very minimal non-genital touch and sometimes no touch at all. They do this by moving their hands *above* their client's body, in that person's energy field. Women have even been known to experience female ejaculation from this kind of energy work. And it's not just sexual healers who can do this.

In my workshops, I teach participants how to facilitate pleasure and orgasmic states for each other without actually touching their partner's body. Initially, some participants express their doubt that this is even possible. But once they actually try it, even the non-believers experience strong effects in their own body or facilitate these effects for their partner.

An energy orgasm can be felt as a whole-body experience or it may be focused in a specific area of the body. And, of course, you can experience an energy orgasm on your own with a little practice.

Embodiment practice – Energy orgasm

This practice will facilitate energy moving in your body and, with a little practice, can be experienced as an orgasm.

1. Lie on your back on a semi-hard surface. Pull your knees up. Start a self-pleasuring practice, incorporating some of the techniques and ideas we covered earlier. Use breath, sounds, hip movement, different kinds of touch, internal stimulation, and so on.

2. Get yourself really aroused but make sure you don't have a clitoral orgasm or even an internal orgasm. You should feel as if you are exploding with orgasmic energy. Then, relax your body and let go of all techniques.

3. Breathe deeply into your belly. Inhale through your nose and exhale through your mouth. Continue this for a few minutes.

4. Visualize your sexual energy as a ball of fire above your genitals. Alternatively, you could visualize it as strong ocean waves. Place your hands in the air above your genitals and try to feel the viscosity of the energy in this area. Experiment with an 'ether touch,' which we covered earlier. Push downwards on your energy body, swirl it around, pull it up and sweep it to your sides.

5. Start moving your hands in a circular motion between your chakras. Explore moving them from each chakra to the next one and also up and down the chakras, constantly keeping your hands above your body to guide the energy as it moves through your body. Experiment with placing one hand above your genitals and having the other pulling invisible energy strings from your heart center, throat, third eye and crown.

6. You can also occasionally place a finger or even your hand on your actual skin near your chakras, not as stimulation but as a way to intensify the energy.

7. You can still incorporate breath, sound, movement, vaginal squeezes, and so on, but make sure you are constantly enhancing the experience with your hands above your body. You can also keep using visualization, but make sure you are also attentive to feeling the energy. Follow your impulses. Pretend you have super powers. Play with the energy.

8. During this practice, you might have emotions come up such as sadness, anger, frustration or confusion. Allow yourself to express whatever you experience fully.

9. And, of course, you might also experience new kinds of pleasure and orgasm. Express this as well. When you feel complete, relax and notice the sensations, energies, emotions, thoughts and insights. Write down your experience in your orgasmic diary.

The next time you do this practice, you could do a very brief self-pleasuring session at the start, or otherwise skip it completely and instead build your sexual energy with the power of your intention and your magic hands floating above your body.

Now, what other orgasms are possible?

The everywhere-else orgasm

There are women who orgasm from every place in their bodies. They can orgasm from caressing their skin, their inner thighs, their chest or the area between the shoulder blades. Maybe orgasm comes about from touching their lower back or licking their earlobes, fingers or toes.

One of my clients orgasmed while I was massaging her Achilles heel, and I soon integrated this into my sensual massage routine. As a result, many other women have experienced this as well. Anybody can be fully orgasmic with the right attitudes and practices.

You might have other areas or spots in your body that produce very distinct sensations of pleasure or orgasm. Keep deepening those experiences and also experiment with other areas and ways to arouse yourself. Anything is possible!

And it's not just touch or particular places in the body that can bring about an orgasm.

Some women experience orgasm while meditating, practicing yoga, singing devotional songs or looking at the sunset. There are women who orgasm when they ride a roller coaster or bungee jump. Other women orgasm when their partner tells them he loves them or when a powerful man holds their hands, looking them deeply in the eyes with love, devotion and presence.

Just for fun, let's have a peek at the diverse orgasmic experiences that women have available to them. Have you ever heard of any of these 'gasms'?

- Yogasm – An orgasm during a yoga practice.
- Food-gasm – Ever had a piece of chocolate and trembled in pleasure? That's a mini orgasm.

- Giggle-gasm – An orgasm that comes as a woman giggles or laughs, sometimes becoming a rolling wave of laughter that feels pleasurable and orgasmic.
- Grief-gasm – Some women experience grief over their separation from a lover or the death of a loved one and the intense energy of their grief can turn into an orgasm.
- Thinking off (as opposed to wanking off) – An orgasm experienced by visualizing the sexual energy in your body.
- Man-gasm – Some women orgasm when a man looks in their eyes with presence and love; they experience an orgasmic state brought about by his masculine presence.
- Music-gasm – An orgasm that comes from listening to a strong or meaningful piece of music.
- Dance-gasm – An orgasm that arises from dancing, and specifically vigorous, energetic and ecstatic forms of dance. (I have met a woman in her sixties that even experiences female ejaculation while dancing.)
- Pain-gasm – Orgasm can be experienced during pain. One of my teachers, Barbara Carellas (author of *Urban Tantra*), recounts the time when she got a tattoo on her ankle and experienced very strong pain. She managed to transform that pain into pleasure and experienced orgasm then and there.
- Birth-gasm – An orgasmic birth is possible. Women who practice conscious birthing can manage to have a very pleasurable birthing experience and many of them experience various states of orgasm.
- Meditation-gasm – An orgasm experienced in a meditative state. When I was living in a yogic community in Thailand, I often attended ten- or seventeen-day meditation retreats. These included many hours of meditation per day, spiritual lectures and yoga. Men and women were separated, silence was maintained throughout

the retreat and participants were asked to avoid touch and even looking at people's faces. Yet still, many women reported they became extremely horny and some experienced peaks of orgasm and even long and intense orgasmic states during the meditation sessions. Some of them were shaking, convulsing and spasming.

All of the information about the different kinds of orgasm is intended to inspire and inform you about what is possible. But try not to be attached to experiencing any or all of them.

Sometimes, just stimulating particular spots on the body will not necessarily be enough to bring about an orgasm. If a woman has trauma or limiting beliefs about her capacity to orgasm, this will likely affect her ability to orgasm. Sometimes, healing work is required to clear any issues and, therefore, enable orgasm.

Orgasm is not something to be forced, but rather something to open up to. Knowing that your orgasmic potential is unlimited and being present with whatever you are experiencing is the most powerful attitude you can cultivate towards your orgasms and everything else in your life.

So, as you can see, you have an unlimited capacity for orgasm in your body when you believe in your orgasmic potential and embody your orgasmic energy with powerful practices. We've come a long way since the beginning of this book, but there is still more to come. No matter how orgasmic you currently are, you can always explore different practices to allow for more orgasmic energy in your body.

The one hour orgasm

By now, you are fully aware of the orgasmic potential of your body. Perhaps you have been practicing some of the techniques I've shared and you might already be experiencing some orgasms beyond the simple clitoral orgasm. Many women will be satisfied with that, and that's okay.

But what I want to share with you is that *an* orgasm is just the beginning. If you are able to experience orgasm, then you can experience multiple orgasms or expand and deepen your orgasm to last long minutes, an hour or even longer. This won't necessarily feel like an orgasmic peak anymore, but more of a long orgasmic state. And although milder, these feel more profound.

I once facilitated a sexual healing session for a German woman in her late twenties. She came to me for assistance because she hardly ever orgasmed. During our session, she was able to experience a few kinds of bodily orgasm – a long and intense orgasmic state, very deep pleasure sensations and a semi-trance state. But that was just the beginning. She stayed in a mild state of bliss for about three days that also included some pleasure sensations and a feeling of energy running through her body.

Many of my clients have had similar experiences to this. These women, and others who have attended my workshops, have been able to experience extended orgasms not because of anything *I did* but because I shared *the idea* that an orgasm can be a prolonged state and not just a momentary peak. Since most of my coaching work is done via Skype, I don't even touch many of my clients; I simply coach and guide them to stay in the orgasm and to deepen it.

The important thing for you to understand is that these results are not about me or my 'magic fingers.' What enables these women to have these orgasmic experiences is an understanding of what an orgasm really is, some techniques that help uncover their full orgasmic potential, and the self-permission to stay in the orgasm and deepen it.

Multiple orgasms are just the beginning

Sometimes, when people become more orgasmic or start practicing sacred sexuality, they begin to experience multiple orgasms or facilitate them for others. Unfortunately, this can bring about a tendency to engage in an amateur sport known as 'orgasm counting.' You might hear these people say something like, 'I gave a woman twenty orgasms' or 'I had thirty orgasms in one session.'

There's nothing wrong with multiple orgasms! It's great to have them, facilitate them for others and to feel good about it too. The problem is that many people stop here, believing that multiple orgasms are the peak of the sexual experience. If you are still able to count your orgasms, they may not be all that strong. And if *he's* counting them, he's missing the point. That is why I sometimes say, 'multiple orgasms are for beginners.'

Once you experience multiple orgasms, it's possible and actually quite easy to experience what I referred to earlier as a 'plateau orgasm' or an 'intense orgasmic state.' You can either experience individual peaks of orgasm that lengthen into an orgasmic state or have so many orgasms that you realize it's just one long *state* of orgasm.

As good as multiple orgasms are, they are just one step along the path that I call the pleasure path or 'the continuum of pleasure.'

The continuum of pleasure

Once you learn to acknowledge and recognize the orgasmic nature of every pleasurable sensation, you can gradually go into much greater depths of pleasure and orgasm. Follow me down the pleasure path for a moment:

- A simple sensation turns into a pleasurable sensation and then into the experience of pleasure.
- Sustained continuous pleasure turns into an orgasm.

- Your orgasm becomes multiple orgasms, peaking every few minutes or even every thirty seconds, usually intensifying from one to the next.
- Orgasmic peaks become successive and very rapid or individual peaks lengthen into one long, continuous orgasm.
- You experience an intense orgasmic state. Sometimes, you can still recognize individual peaks, but even the 'valleys' between the peaks are an orgasmic experience by themselves.
- Usually, the continuous orgasmic state is intense and physical initially but gradually becomes subtler, with fewer physical manifestations and less body awareness.
- When one continuous orgasm becomes deep enough and long enough, it can turn into a meditative orgasmic state.
- Staying in a meditative orgasmic state for a long time is a mild expression of enlightenment.

Therefore, a small wave of pleasure can lead you to a kind of enlightenment on the continuum of pleasure.

Sensation > Pleasure wave > Mild orgasmic state > Orgasm > Multiple orgasms > Intense orgasmic state > Meditative orgasmic state > Enlightenment. *(see Diagram 15 on page 202)*

The continuum of pleasure

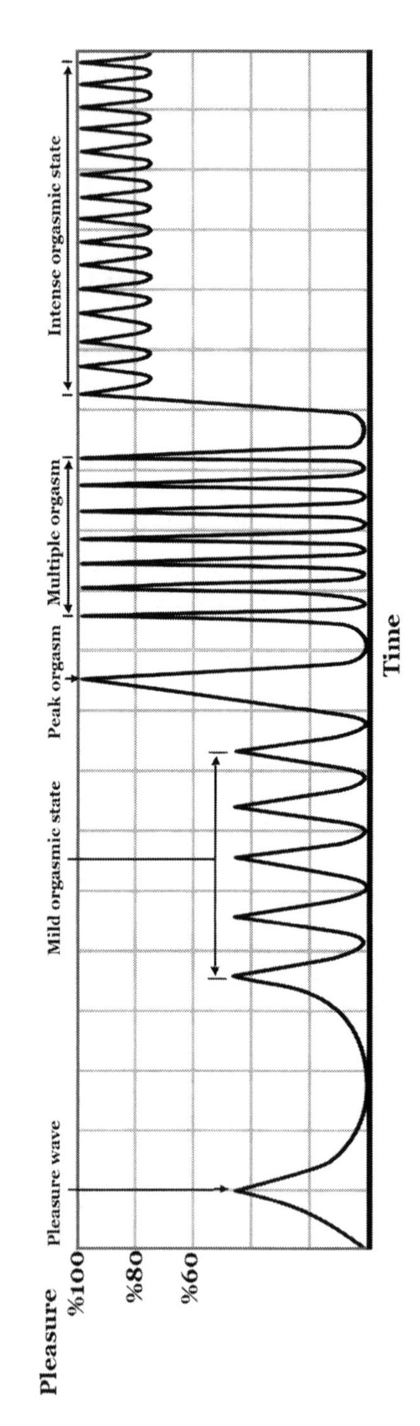

Diagram 15

It's important to understand that a one-hour-long orgasm isn't the same as sixty orgasms that last only one minute. As you orgasm for longer and longer periods of time, the nature of the orgasm changes. You experience levels of pleasure that you didn't imagine were possible. The orgasmic energy spreads throughout your body and creates a continuous whole-body orgasm. It also goes up your chakras so you experience different chakra-related orgasms and expands outwards throughout your five bodies so you experience the orgasm not just on the physical level, but also on the energetic, emotional and spiritual/causal levels. The orgasm becomes a transcendent, spiritual experience. You become aware of the highest aspect of yourself beyond name, identity and ego.

Knowing what's possible and having an orgasmic attitude is fundamental to expanding and deepening the orgasmic experiences you have. And the first limitation to address is the time pressure and expectation many women place on orgasm.

Remove the orgasm timer

One of the greatest insights I have had while working with women is that many have an internal timer that 'tells' them, 'This orgasm has finished; you have 'come' and your orgasm is over.'

For most people, an orgasm lasts a few seconds or, at most, half a minute. Then the orgasm timer kicks in and you start to think something along these lines:

'Oh, I've been orgasming for a while, it's probably over.'

'I'm not worthy of more pleasure; I don't deserve it.'

'I've orgasmed and now I need to pleasure him.'

'Sex is finished because I have had an orgasm.'

'He's probably waiting for me to finish.'

This unhelpful timer is created by the following beliefs and attitudes:

- Most women and men believe that an orgasm is a momentary experience – you rise, you peak, you fall. They don't know that an orgasm can be a continuous state. Not many are aware that an orgasmic state can last long minutes and sometimes hours.
- The traditional sexual response model is desire > arousal > orgasm > resolution. But this only allows orgasm to be a short moment followed by a resolution or an inevitable end.
- Orgasm is seen as the goal of sex, so once it's achieved, it signals the end of the sexual interaction.
- Women are used to having clitoral orgasms, which generally last fifteen to thirty seconds. So even when they do experience another kind of orgasm, they believe that it will be as short and fleeting as their clitoral orgasm, so their timer kicks in and brings about a premature end to their orgasm.
- Women compare their orgasm to a man's ejaculatory orgasm, which lasts about ten to twenty seconds. It is characterized by a strong peak followed by a sharp decline of pleasure, loss of erection and a kind of shutting down.
- Some women feel obliged to 'give back' once they have had their orgasm and are not comfortable being or remaining in a receptive state.
- Sometimes, an orgasm becomes stronger the longer it lasts. Some women have a subconscious fear that it's 'too much' or they 'can't handle it,' so they make themselves snap out of it.
- Some women can't bear to stay in the open and vulnerable state of the orgasm, so they exercise control in order to end it.

These beliefs and understandings create an orgasm timer that limits your orgasmic experience. Here's a scenario that regularly occurs in my sessions:

I facilitate a sexual healing session for a woman. She orgasms. I notice she's starting to drop off the orgasm. I tell her, 'You are still coming.' She says, 'No, I'm not.' A few seconds later, her body shakes or convulses and she says, 'Oh, yes, I am.' She then enters an orgasmic state, which goes on for minutes, and sometimes longer.

> *'There I was, a person who not so long ago felt almost asexual and pleasure-phobic, in a sort of full body orgasm that lasted for more than two hours.'*

Women commonly bring about the premature ending of an orgasmic peak by perceiving it as something that has already happened and has faded away. But by changing your attitude and understanding orgasm as an opening, a portal or the entrance to a range of sensations and pleasures, you can make the transition into extended orgasmic states and multiple orgasms.

The good news is that once you are aware of your tendency of cutting your orgasm short, you are able to 'remove the orgasm timer' by affirming a new set of attitudes.

Attitudes that support extended orgasms

I invite you to try on the following attitudes for size and notice how they can shift your orgasmic experience:

- An orgasm is a state, not just a momentary occurrence or 'peak.'
- The peak is just the beginning; an orgasm can be deepened and expanded from a single peak into a high 'plateau.'
- Orgasm can be experienced as whole-body pleasure, not just a momentary and localized 'peak.'

- The moments before and after a 'peak' are also an orgasmic experience, which can be deepened and expanded.
- Every small wave of pleasure is an orgasmic experience, like a mini-orgasm, and this understanding allows orgasmic states to be experienced more easily.
- Extended orgasms require an avoidance of clitoral orgasms, given they deplete energy and entrench a pattern of arousal, peak and resolution.
- Relaxation and letting go is the key; the body knows what to do.
- Openness, acceptance and surrender are critical. Let go of control.
- Extended orgasms can feel very intense, overwhelming or 'too much.' Opening and surrendering to the experience is required.
- Intensity is to be embraced and relaxed into without needing to understand it or control it.

These attitudes are the ones I share with my clients that enable them to experience deeper and extended orgasms. They are foundational to any techniques that are used to support orgasm. So once you embody an orgasmic attitude, you can easily deepen your orgasms with a few simple techniques, many of which we have explored earlier in this book.

How to expand your orgasm?

Expanding your orgasm uses similar techniques to orgasming for the first time. So, let's recap the techniques that not only support orgasm, but also enable you to expand and deepen your orgasm into an orgasmic state and engulf your whole body with pleasure:

- Relax – This is so important. So many people and even teachers focus on technique, effort and movement. I want to make it crystal clear that one of the most important things you can 'do' in your sex life is to learn how to relax. When you are relaxed, you can get more aroused. Then, if you stay relaxed, you are better able to orgasm and keep orgasming. I know that relaxing is easier said than done, but if you know and remember that this is one of the most crucial elements of orgasm, you might just allow yourself to relax rather than worrying about some acrobatic orgasm technique.

- Breathe – Full belly breaths are important. You can experiment with the techniques of fast mouth breathing and full retention, as described in the *Breath* topic earlier. When you are holding a full breath in, send it down to your genitals.

- Continuous sound – As you are starting to orgasm, take a deep breath and make a continuous 'Aaaaaaaahhhhhhhhhh' sound. Inhale quickly and exhale slowly, with sound. This is a way to stay focused, keep the energy moving and open the throat chakra. It also to tricks your subconscious into believing, 'There is a sound, so I'm probably still orgasming.' Explore other sounds described in the earlier *Sound* topic.

- Movement – Create gentle convulsions through your spine; move your hips back and forth, side to side, in circles and bounce them on ground. Check out the earlier *Movement* topic for more ideas here.

- Touch – Use the five elements to touch yourself while you are orgasming, or focus on the element that works best for you. Also explore the element that challenges you, because it might be the missing ingredient.

- Express your emotions – Many women don't orgasm or don't experience deep orgasms because they stop themselves from expressing their emotions. They constrict their breath and their throat. You should keep breathing, relax your jaw and throat, and make sounds to express what you are feeling.

- Focus on the sensations – Some women 'lose' their orgasm because their mind drifts away. Keep focusing on the sensations in your body. Remember that where awareness goes, energy flows.
- Ride the wave – One of the main ideas or techniques you can use to expand your orgasms is to see an orgasm like a wave in the ocean. You need to 'ride the wave' of pleasure sensations and stay on the wave in order to stay in the orgasm. If your orgasm is decreasing in intensity, intensify the arousal so you stay on the orgasmic wave.
- Use the 'edging' technique – You can practice 'edging' and 'the pause' to help stay on the verge of orgasm for longer periods. You will notice that the whole experience becomes an orgasmic experience. This is what I call a 'mild orgasmic state.'
- Keep it 'down there' – If you tend to 'lose' your orgasm because all of your sexual energy shoots up to your higher chakras, practice keeping your energy in your genital area. You can do this by pressing your hand on your labia, squeezing your muscles, bouncing your buttocks on the mattress and, most importantly, keeping the focus of your mind in your yoni. Keep doing this while you are orgasming and between orgasms. Your sexual energy will stay in your genitals and allow you to keep orgasming, while some of it will still shoot up and spread to your entire body.
- Keep stimulating – Many women orgasm and then stop stimulating and moving. This is related to the 'orgasm timer' and to an entrenched, limiting belief that says that an orgasm happens once and signifies the end of the sexual experience. Instead, keep doing whatever gets you to orgasm, both during and after your orgasm. This might keep the orgasm going, or facilitate another orgasm within a few seconds.
- Vaginal contractions – Contracting your vaginal muscles can bring about an orgasm. When you start to orgasm, keep your

muscles contracted while you have the orgasm and as long as you can. This keeps the sexual energy flowing and gives a message to your subconscious that, 'My vagina is contracting so I'm probably still orgasming.' This can make your orgasms longer and stronger. Remember to completely relax your vagina before and during orgasms at other times.

- Visualization – Imagine that you are climbing a hill. The hill represents the level of your pleasure and orgasm. Use some of the techniques above so you rise up the hill. Don't focus on the effort. Keep stoking your orgasmic fire as you are orgasming. Go even higher. At times, you can allow yourself to plateau for a few minutes, but then keep climbing. The higher you get, the better the view.
- Orgasmic affirmations – When you are about to orgasm, say something like, 'I'm coming, I'm coming,' and keep repeating it even when you feel your orgasm has subsided. You could also try saying, 'Yes ... yes ... yes.' If you are with a partner, ask him to repeatedly say things as you are orgasming, such as, 'You are still coming ... yes ... you can stay there ... stay on the wave.' (For more couple-practices, check out the online resources section at www.intimatepower.com/orgasm-book-resources).

These techniques all help to expand and deepen orgasm into much longer and stronger states. Explore different intensities of breath, sound, touch, movement and feeling – the stronger, faster and deeper you are able to breathe, move, make sounds and touch yourself, the stronger, deeper, longer and more frequent (multiple) your orgasms can be. Remember that this is a phase along your orgasmic journey. Soon you will be able to orgasm without much intensity, and that is ultimately the most natural state of orgasm – effortless, relaxed and continuous.

Embodiment practice – Expand your orgasm

You've learned all the important techniques and attitudes to expand your orgasm. Now it's time to put it all together.

1. Set aside two hours for this practice. Disconnect the phone. Set up the space.
2. Start a self-pleasuring ritual and include internal stimulation.
3. Build your pleasure for half an hour without allowing yourself to orgasm. Keep staying on the edge.
4. After half an hour, allow yourself to orgasm but use all the techniques and attitudes above to keep your orgasm going. Keep using breath, sound, movement, touch and stimulation to keep a high level of pleasure. Use the 'visualization' technique to keep climbing the hill of orgasm.
5. Keep pumping the pleasure even when it feels 'too much.' At the beginning, it will feel like effort, but gradually allow yourself to relax into the ecstasy.
6. If you're not experiencing a continuous orgasm, don't worry about it. Keep going anyway. Enjoy the ride.
7. At times you might feel like you've had 'enough.' It's ok to stop, but if you can experience more pleasure and an even stronger orgasm, why would you stop? Recognize that this might be the 'orgasm timer' and keep going. Aim to keep a high level of intensity for about an hour. This is the 'intense orgasmic state' that I've described earlier in the book.
8. After an hour or even longer, allow yourself to completely relax. Be aware of how your body is feeling, of sensations and emotions. Allow yourself to integrate the insights you gained from this experience. Send the energy to any place in your body that needs it, to any event in your past that needs healing, to any aspect of

your life that can benefit from it, to your loved ones, and to any place in the world where there is suffering. This is sex magic. Ultimately, dedicate and send this energy to God, the universe, the cosmic consciousness or to whatever you consider to be your highest value or principal.

9. Notice that your orgasm might keep going much longer after you stop the strong stimulation and movement. Allow that to happen. Gradually allow yourself to go into the 'meditative orgasmic state.' Stay in this state for as long as you can.
10. Note your experience in your orgasmic diary. Really take time to describe as much as possible; this is such a special state of consciousness that you might forget it if you don't write it down
11. Allow yourself to rest and integrate after this strong and meaningful experience.

Keep incorporating these ideas and practices into your daily self-pleasuring and your love-making, and witness your orgasms becoming deeper, stronger and *much* longer.

Now, let's explore a few special orgasmic practices that will expand your orgasmic experience even further.

Special orgasmic practices

We have already covered so many orgasmic ideas and practices that you can use to ignite and unleash your orgasms. The following practices will allow you to go even further on your orgasmic journey.

Micro-cosmic orbit

The micro-cosmic orbit is a practice from the Taoist tradition that combines breath, visualization and focus of the mind. It can help you to move your sexual energies away from your genitals or keep your orgasm going for longer.

Embodiment practice – Micro-cosmic orbit

People who were complete beginners have done this exercise at my workshop and have become aroused, experienced mild pleasure or even started convulsing and shaking with orgasm. The original Tao practice is much more detailed but this shorter and simpler version works beautifully.

1. Sit comfortably and close your eyes.
2. Visualize a circuit of energy that goes from your head, down the front of your body to your genitals and then up the back of your body to the top of your head. Don't just visualize the energy, try to actually feel it moving down your front and up your back. If it helps make it clearer, move your hand lightly in sync with the movement. Then let go of the hand movement. Only once you have a clear image of this energy circuit should you continue to the next phase of this practice.
3. Incorporate breath into your energy circuit. Exhale completely and bring your awareness to the top of your head. Inhale slowly and, as you do, visualize your breath carrying energy down the front of your body to your yoni. Then exhale and move the energy up the back of your body to the top of your head again. Inhale again down the front of your body, and so on. Once you are comfortable with this, continue to the next phase.
4. Incorporate vaginal squeezes into your circuit. Head … inhale … down front … squeeze genitals … exhale … up back … head … release squeeze … inhale … down front, and so on. As you are squeezing, visualize pushing or shooting your sexual energy from your genitals up your spine.

5. Do this practice for five to ten minutes at a time. When you're finished, describe your experience in your orgasmic diary.

Some people respond more to physical practices and others to visualization practices. Give this a try and see if it works for you. This is a great practice to incorporate into your self-pleasuring, love-making and meditation practices to help yourself become more aware of your energy and learn how to move it around your body. *(see Diagram 16 on page 214)*

Microcosmic orbit

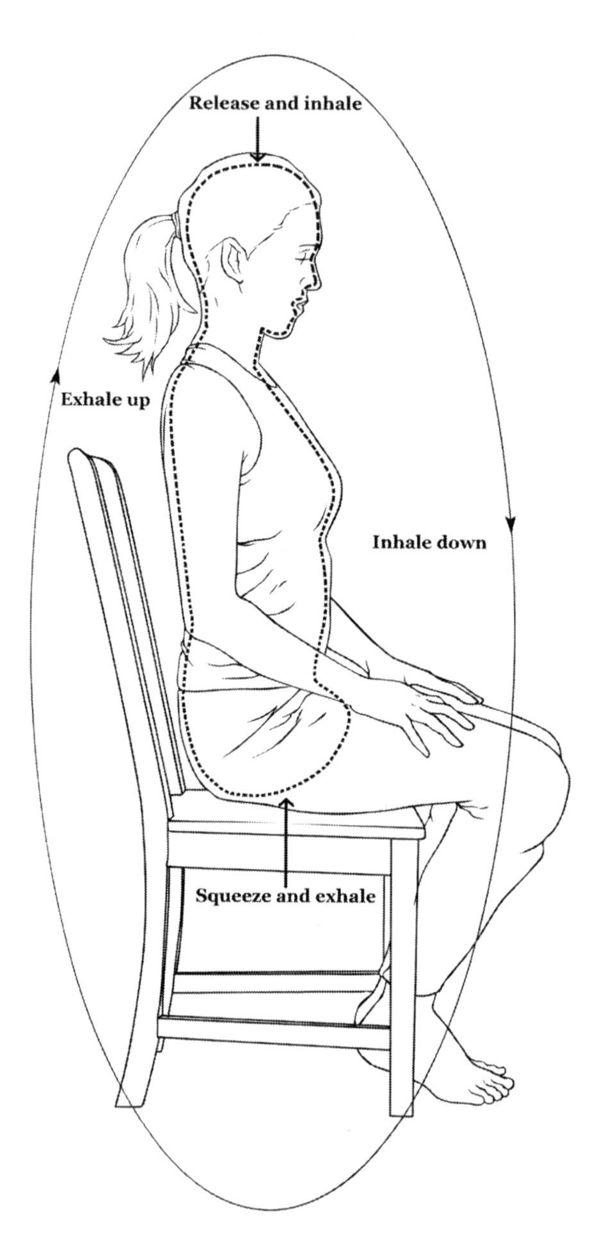

Diagram 16

Female ejaculation

Female ejaculation is an orgasmic experience that you may want to explore. When some women get really aroused, they can expel liquid from their urethra or vagina in quantities that range from a few drops to a cupful. There is a lot of debate in scientific circles about the nature of this liquid. Some scientists claim that female ejaculation is caused by urinary incontinence. I do not agree.

There are a few kinds of liquids that a woman can expel from her genital area:

- **Vaginal lubrication** – Some women produce so much vaginal lubrication that it can be mistaken as ejaculation.
- **Urine** – Some women simply urinate when they are really aroused or when they experience a strong orgasm because they relax all muscle control and surrender into the experience. Society regards pee as bodily waste and there's a lot of shame concerning pee in this context. But there is actually no problem with pee. It is even used by yogis as a form of natural medicine that can be ingested or applied to the skin. (Look up urine therapy or amaroli.) Ejaculating urine is often not distinguished from other kinds of female ejaculation and it can be a pleasurable feeling of release and letting go.
- **Thick female ejaculatory fluid** – This is a thick, slightly milky, odorous fluid, which is sometimes expelled after strong clitoral stimulation as an aspect of explosive orgasm. It's usually expelled in one strong 'gush.' It doesn't smell or taste particularly great. After the ejaculation, the woman can become hypersensitive in her clit, feeling satisfied to a degree but not interested in continuing the sexual interaction. This is similar to male ejaculation in terms of energy loss. Women also lose energy when they ejaculate this liquid. As discussed earlier, clitoral stimulation is great, but clitoral orgasms cause a loss of vital energy.

- **'Real' female ejaculation** – This is a clear, light liquid that smells and tastes slightly sweet. It sometimes also smells a little like urine and there might be traces of urine in it. But if you compare it to your urine before and after the sexual experience, you will notice that it looks, smells and tastes completely different. Some scientific studies have described this liquid as a diluted form of urine without the element of ammonia, which gives urine its characteristic pungent smell and taste. This type of ejaculation can be expelled from the urethra or the vagina or both. Some people claim that it's expelled from small openings near the vagina called 'Bartholin's gland' or 'Skene's gland.' Personally, I doubt that this is the main source of the liquid.

  The liquid is not viscous at all and, therefore, actually decreases vaginal and genital lubrication. This form of ejaculation is related to G-spot stimulation and orgasm. Sometimes ejaculations are accompanied by pleasure and orgasm and at other times they occur without experiencing orgasm or even pleasure. In Tantra, this liquid is called 'Amrita,' which means something along the lines of 'The nectar of the Goddess.' The Tantrics believe that the sexual energy is transformed into a liquid, which is then expelled from a woman's vagina. There is no loss of energy during this type of ejaculation and a woman can keep ejaculating or orgasming for many minutes. However, this liquid is still charged with energy and some claim it also has some psychoactive effects. It is recommended that the woman or her partner ingest it or apply it to the skin.

- **Cervical ejaculation** – According to some sources, there is also a rare kind of female ejaculation that is expelled from a woman's cervix in very small quantities (just a few drops) that is milky and sweet. It is considered the most refined and sublime form of female ejaculation and is related to deep cervical-uterine orgasms. I have only witnessed this a few times.

How women ejaculate

There are three ways that a woman can ejaculate:

1. The most common way is to apply strong stimulation or pressure to the vagina and specifically to the G-spot area. Some women's G-spot areas swell considerably after stimulation and then it's possible to 'milk' the area to produce ejaculation. Some women describe a feeling of needing their G-spots to be 'milked,' like a kind of pressure that they can't dissipate by themselves.
2. A better way to ejaculate is to learn to squeeze your vaginal muscles to support ejaculation. Some women can ejaculate almost at will when they are aroused enough.
3. Some women ejaculate without trying. It happens without strong stimulation and without squeezing their vaginal muscles. Their pleasure or orgasm induces natural vaginal contractions that create female ejaculation.

If you are an ejaculator and you make love with a new partner, try to tell him in advance about this. Explain that it's a symbol of your pleasure and trust in him. Most men aren't aware of this phenomenon and might think that you are peeing on them.

Some women produce so much liquid that they can easily destroy a mattress. So it's a good idea to always keep plenty of thick towels next to you when explore ejaculation. I know of a couple who made love in an inflatable kids pool because it was the only way they could contain the vast amounts of liquid.

If you want to explore female ejaculation, the following practices will help you to learn how. There are three main practices that might get you to ejaculate. You can consider incorporating one or all of them into your self-pleasure practice.

Embodiment practice – Learning to urinate during sexual activity

Many women don't ejaculate or don't orgasm because they can't let go during self-pleasure or sex. Learning to urinate when you are aroused will help you to relax, accept your body and your bodily secretions, and can create pleasure or even orgasm.

1. Drink about a liter of water. That's about five large glasses.
2. Place a bunch of thick towels on the mattress. For extra protection, consider placing a plastic sheet between the towels and the mattress. If you absolutely can't urinate in bed, try to do this in the shower, bath or on the toilet.
3. Do a self-pleasuring ritual with internal stimulation, getting yourself very aroused and on the edge of orgasm.
4. Pause any pressure and stimulation, remove your fingers or dildo from your yoni and try to urinate. It might take you a few minutes to 'shift gears.' Try not to let out all your urine.
5. After you manage to urinate like this, drink another half liter to a liter of water. Arouse yourself once again to the edge of orgasm.
6. Then, with your fingers or dildo still inside you, try to urinate.
7. Arouse yourself again. Then, try to urinate while you are stimulating yourself internally.
8. Finally, try to urinate while you are orgasming.

Write your experiences in your orgasmic diary.

The purpose of this exercise isn't to urinate during sex, but rather to teach you to relax and let go while you are aroused, being stimulated, being penetrated or while you are orgasming. Of course, if you or your partner are aroused by pee (some people are), then by all means enjoy that while you are having sex.

Embodiment practice – Using stimulation to bring on ejaculation

This practice shows how you can use stimulation to bring on ejaculation.

1. Start a self-pleasuring ritual, getting really aroused and stimulating yourself internally with your fingers.
2. Notice if your G-spot becomes engorged or if you have the feeling of needing to pee when you are stimulating this area.
3. Then squeeze your G-spot with your fingers. The easiest way to do this is to insert your middle and ring fingers to your yoni and squeeze upwards towards your pubic bone or your clit. You can simply squeeze the tissue, or slide your finger along this tissue in a kind of milking movement. You can also spread your fingers in a 'V' shape and do the same. If your fingers get tired, you can use a dildo.
4. You may or may not ejaculate but that is not the goal. Just keep arousing yourself and massaging your G-spot.
5. If you do ejaculate, spread the liquid over your skin and, if you're ready for it, try to taste it. Remember, this is a sacred liquid.

If you have a partner or an open-minded friend, they can give you a yoni massage and use these techniques to help you ejaculate. It's much easier for someone else to do it because of the easier access to your vagina.

I recommend trying this practice both by yourself and with another person if possible. This allows you to have the experience by yourself as well as a slightly different experience when you receive it from another person in a way that you can't facilitate for yourself. After you explore ejaculating by using your fingers, the next stage is to use your internal muscles.

Embodiment practice – Using your muscles to ejaculate

After practicing how to urinate during self-pleasure and squeezing your G-spot area, you may be able to ejaculate. Once you can do this, this practice will help you to ejaculate using just your vaginal muscles.

1. Do a self-pleasuring ritual with internal stimulation and bring yourself close to orgasm.

2. Then incorporate the push-pull vaginal squeeze exercise. Contract and pull your vaginal muscles inwards and then push them outwards. Keep doing this while you are stimulating yourself both externally and internally. You can also use the previous practice of squeezing your G-spot area with your fingers.

3. Allow yourself to orgasm while you are doing this. Keep doing the push-pull action as you are orgasming and use the other techniques mentioned earlier in the *Go ahead, expand your orgasm* topic to keep your orgasm going.

4. Keep doing steps two and three above for about twenty minutes. At this point, you might or might not ejaculate. But don't be attached to any outcome. Simply regard this as a special self-pleasuring ritual.

5. If you do ejaculate, I invite you to taste your ejaculation fluid and smear it over your face and body. Keep going with your stimulation, squeezes and movements because an ejaculation isn't the end of the experience.

6. When you feel complete, lie back and completely relax your body. Become aware of all the sensations and feelings in your body. Write them down in your orgasmic diary.

Female ejaculation is just one of many orgasmic practices that you may wish to explore and these practices will help you to do this.

Although female ejaculation is a beautiful experience and great to practice, you shouldn't worry too much if you can't ejaculate easily or even at all. Too many women, and men, become focused on getting a woman to ejaculate and it becomes a kind of sport or a box to tick. Whatever your current experience with female ejaculation is, accept it and move on to other orgasmic explorations of your journey.

Anal stimulation

Anal stimulation is something you might want to explore. The anus is an important erogenous zone that can bring you a different kind of pleasure. It can also accumulate a lot of stagnant energy that can only be released by actual stimulation. Anal stimulation can help you to move heavy energy away from your genitals.

> *'I personally accumulate a lot of energy in the anal area, which makes me super horny and crazy if I can't release it. The only thing that works is direct stimulation (massage or penetration).'*

You can include anal stimulation as part of your self-pleasuring practice, or do it in isolation. When you do stimulate yourself anally, make sure that you are not touching your yoni with the finger or object that touched your anus, as this might cause infections in your vagina.

If you have never explored anal stimulation, and have some resistance to it, I suggest that there can be great meaning and importance in trying it. It might be worth seeing how it goes as a part of your orgasmic journey.

Sublimation

We have been discussing in detail how to build and maintain sexual energy in various ways. Cultivating sexual energy is great, but it's also important to move it, channel it or, as my tantric teachers say, 'sublime it.'

Sublimation means taking heavy, raw, vital energy from the lower chakras and turning it into a subtle, refined and light energy in the higher chakras. This is how you can move your sexual energy and use it to charge other areas of your life.

For example, you can use this practice when you are turning clitoral stimulation into internal orgasms. Sublimation will help you move the sharp, intense clitoral energy away from your genitals and transform it into whole-body energy that can then become a whole-body orgasm. Or perhaps use this practice if you finish a self-pleasuring practice and you feel either heavy with sexual energy or so charged that you can't think straight. Some of my clients say they can't sleep at night because of the sexual energy they've unleashed. Sublimation can shift this energy.

It's not only energies that can be sublimed. Strong emotions such as fear, confusion, restlessness, sadness and anger are all related to the lower chakras and can be sublimed into the higher chakras, transforming them into love, creativity, mental clarity and oneness.

So, how is this done? Well, nearly any position where your head is lower than your genitals will have some subliming effect. You can start by standing and bending down to hold the back of your knees with your hands. You can also seek the guidance of a yoga teacher who can share yogic techniques of shoulder stand, plow pose and head stand.

The practice of sublimation can be truly life changing because you learn to channel energy in a way that prevents you from being a slave of your hormones and emotions.

Orgasmic extras

For more orgasmic ideas and practices, including special tantric techniques, check out the resources section of my website (www.intimatepower.com/orgasm-book-resources).

There are so many practices you can use in the privacy of your bedroom that help to unleash your orgasmic power, and we've covered some very effective ones in this book. But let's also look at what you can do outside your home and how that can change your life and enhance your orgasmic experience.

7

Living an orgasmic life

One of my core messages on the orgasmic journey is that to be more feminine, sexual and orgasmic, you need to integrate these aspects into your daily life. These practices will naturally transform your life, so your life also needs to transform in a way that supports and aligns with your orgasmic practice. This way, your private and public life are supporting each other. This is the final aspect of my 'holistic transformation model' – transform.

Many women create a separation between their sex life and their daily life. They might be very sexual, horny and orgasmic behind closed doors, but in their public life they put on a shy, virginal, prude, pseudo-spiritual or even asexual mask. But this creates a kind of inner-conflict that prevents them from living life as an empowered and integrated woman.

The more you make your life orgasmic, that more orgasmic you become. The more orgasmic you are, the more your life changes.

There are four lifestyle changes that will help you to live a fully orgasmic life:

1. Engage in activities that support and deepen your orgasmic practice.
2. Make lifestyle changes that support your orgasmic practice.
3. Express your femininity, sensuality, sexuality and orgasmic nature in your daily life.
4. Speak up.

Let's discuss each one in a little detail and how it relates to your journey as an orgasmic woman. I invite you to consider the ideas presented and come up with others that feel right for you.

Orgasmic activities

Here are some ideas for activities you may already engage in or might like to try:

- A hobby with artistic creativity – Express your femininity, emotions or opinions through your art. You don't have to be good or professional or even show your art to anyone. Create art for yourself as a way to express yourself.
- Dancing – Dance every day by yourself for at least ten minutes. Put on your favorite sexy music and crank the volume up if you can. Express the different aspects of your femininity through your dance. Also, dance a few times a week in public. This forms a part of your 'orgasmic movement' practice.
- Singing – Open your throat chakra and develop more courage and self-confidence. Enjoy singing without caring how musical you are or what people think. Sing on your own or consider going to public singing events or classes, like devotional singing. Go to a rock or folk concert and enjoy the anonymity and the high volume of the speakers; sing your heart out. It's also a great opportunity to shout if you need to.

- Meditate daily – When I say 'meditate,' I mean silent, still, sitting, eyes-closed, introspective meditation. Not modern interpretations such as ecstatic meditation, shaking meditation, music meditation, and so on. Consider joining a bona-fide meditation course such as advaita-vedanta, vipasana, dzog-chen or any other tradition that focuses on consciousness and awareness as the object of meditation. This will help you relax and also help you to witness intensity without reacting to it or running away from it. You can also seek introspective meditation practices that are in line with your current spiritual or religious practice if this is important to you.
- Yoga – Practice yoga to activate and bring awareness to your entire body. Most forms of yoga in the west are just glorified exercise, so try to find a yoga teacher or studio that incorporates and teaches the spiritual aspects of yoga. Yoga positions should be held comfortably without effort for a few minutes at a time. If you are sweating a lot during a yoga class, it probably means it's exercise.
- Exercise – Consider some kind of cardio activity such as jogging, swimming, going to the gym, Pilates or one of the exercise-related forms of yoga, such as Bikram (hot yoga) or Vinyasa-flow. As long as you don't hurt yourself, these forms of yoga are some of the best forms of all-body exercise you can find for cardio, strength and flexibility. Try to find activities that you can do by yourself and activities you can do with friends or at a studio. Exercise improves circulation, oxygenation and waste-removal and, therefore, improves your ability to orgasm, makes you happier and improves your body image.
- Spend time in nature – Find ways to spend more time in nature, be it your garden, a nearby park or driving out of town for a few hours or a whole weekend. Instead of sitting in a cafe, you can sit on a blanket or even a few newspapers at the park. Camping in nature is amazing. Nature is the feminine. It nourishes your body and soul on a deep level. Even walking in a frozen forest in the dead of winter connects you to nature.

- Try to receive a massage at least once a month, and more often if possible, to support your practice of 'touch.' Alternate between relaxing massage and therapeutic massage such as osteo or deep tissue.
- Take long showers and hot baths. Bathe in the ocean or at least in a pool. Don't worry about doing laps. Just enjoy the water. Visit the sauna or a hot spring from time to time if that is accessible for you.
- Consider creating a kind of daily routine to supports your orgasmic journey. For example:
  - Ten minutes of shaking, dancing or exercising.
  - At least twenty minutes of self-pleasuring with internal stimulation (and aim for forty-five minutes twice a week).
  - Twenty minutes of sitting meditation.
  - Ten minutes of journaling, affirmations and intention-setting.

These activities by themselves won't help you have mind-blowing orgasms, however, in combination with your other orgasmic practices, they will have a noticeable effect on your pleasure and sex life.

Activities are one of the things you can do to support your orgasmic journey and the next thing to look at is what aspects of your lifestyle you can change or let go of.

Orgasmic lifestyle choices

Take a good look at your whole lifestyle. Identify what doesn't serve you or your orgasmic practice, and then make a change or get rid of it. Here are some key lifestyle aspects I recommend having a look at:

- **Friends** – Are your friends supportive? Do they accept you as a person and as an expressive, orgasmic, sexual and feminine woman? Are they empowering to be around? Are they people that inspire you? Do they lift you up or bring you down? Are your girlfriends juicy, orgasmic and feminine *or* frigid, ball-busting and man-hating?

  Let go of the people in your life that don't accept you, support you, inspire you and empower you to be the woman that you want to be.

- **Clothing** – Do your clothes express and celebrate your beauty, sexiness, femininity and sexuality? Are you happy wearing your clothes?

  I'm not saying that women constantly need to wear clothes that sexualize them. By all means, your cloths should be comfortable and you could also have some sexy clothes or lingerie for special occasions. But most of your clothes should at least make you look good, feel good and help to express your femininity. You might consider wearing sexy underwear if that feels good for you. As a side note, women who wear high heel shoes just to look good and are not comfortable – shouldn't. Learn to embrace your height and enjoy wearing shoes that support your body and allow you to move freely. And then occasionally wear high heels if you want to express that part of yourself.

  Wear clothes that allow you to breathe effortlessly and deeply into your lower belly. Find clothes that allow you to touch your skin and if possible have access to your erogenous zones.

- **Home** – Is your home an expression of who you are? Does your home feel feminine and sexual? What can you do in or around your home so it feels more 'you'?

Also, try to keep your house clean and organized without being a cleaning fanatic. Make sure you get rid of whatever you don't really need. Get rid of clutter. Don't hoard.

- **Geographical location** – Are you in a place, neighborhood, city, region, country or continent that supports you as a person, as a woman and as a sexual being? Are you living in an orthodox Christian, Muslim, Jewish or another religious community that aims to control you and your femininity? Does the weather make you feel expanded or contracted? Are the people around you inspiring or depressing?

  I'm aware that leaving, moving and starting again in a new place is a huge change. But maybe taking such a huge step is exactly the thing that will change your life and allow you to discover, express and be who you really are. I left Israel in 2001 and have spent time in Asia, Australia and Europe. Travelling and living in foreign countries has helped me grow into who I am now, and has allowed me to study, practice and share the ideas and techniques that led to the book that you're reading today.

- **Career** – Do you do what you love? Are you able to express your talents and gifts in your job or business? Are you able to express your feminine gifts, such as love, receptivity and nurturing, in your work? Are you doing what your soul yearns to do? Are you genuinely fulfilled?

  Some people are able to work just for the money and don't need fulfillment from their job. But to live a truly holistic and balanced life, it's important to bring all aspects of your life into alignment with who you are, with your talents and gifts. Career is something that we spend a third to a half of our waking hours on. If your career isn't deeply fulfilling you, if you aren't expressing your highest gifts and really helping others, consider making a gradual career change and maybe even becoming self-employed or running your own business. Your expanding sexual energy and rising confidence will make it easier for you to do that.

If you are inspired to harness your sexual energy and newfound confidence to share your gift, help others and rock your business, look for my writing on 'conscious business' in the resources section of my website (www.intimatepower.com/orgasm-book-resources).

- **Health** – A strong and healthy body is able to orgasm more easily, frequently, deeply and strongly. It also contributes to your body image. Adopt healthy habits of living, sleeping and eating.

  Try to minimize your consumption of animal products, packaged and processed foods, non-organic food and genetically modified food (GM/GMO). Increase your consumption of organic vegetables, fruits, whole grains, nuts, seeds and cold-pressed oils. Include some raw foods in your diet. Don't get too stressed or go overboard with diet though. If you have fries or a chocolate cake once a week, it won't kill you.

- **Medications** – Try to find alternative solutions to any medications you take. Specifically, try to avoid anti-depressants such as SSRIs, which decrease your ability to orgasm. The interesting thing is that orgasm can improve your wellbeing and decrease depression. (I'm referring to implosive orgasms; explosive clitoral orgasms can make you moody, emotional, chaotic or even more depressed.) Consult with your therapist about going off your medications, but be aware that he or she will probably not be supportive of this course of action. After all, their worldview and their income is based on medicating you and seeing you once or twice a month for the rest of your life. Again, I'm no doctor, so you need to make the right decision for yourself.

- **The pill** – The birth control pill might be one of the easiest and safest solutions to avoid getting pregnant, but it also can harm your libido, decrease your vaginal lubrication and make it more difficult for you to orgasm. Moreover, it decreases your connection to your body and feminine intuition. It also changes your natural intuition about potential partners. Educate yourself about alternative or natural contraceptive methods.

- **Intra Uterine Devices (IUD)** – I hate to say it, but this is another contraceptive method that I don't recommend. Copper coils can attract electro-magnetic radiation from cell phones, Wi-Fi networks or any other electrical device in and around your home. And hormonal IUDs have similar side effects to birth control pills. Also, both coils can create a constant irritation in your cervix or womb and lead to a mild infection. As always, you are responsible for your body and need to find a birth control method that serves you.

It's understandable that you won't be able to change all aspects of your life in one day. All I am suggesting is that you experiment with these ideas, incorporate more of them into your life and remember to have fun along the way.

Lifestyle choices do have an impact on your orgasmic experience and so does your ability to express your femininity in every moment.

Have an orgasmic day

Find ways to express your sensuality and sexuality throughout the day in various ways and settings. Here are some ideas:

- Touch yourself whenever you can. Place a hand on your breasts or genitals as you are driving or working on your laptop. If you can't touch your genitals and breasts, you can caress your hair or massage your neck or feet.
- Keep connecting to *her*. Love your yoni, your pussy, your vagina, your womb. Ask her how she feels and what she wants.

- Every time you go to the toilet, spend an extra few minutes touching your yoni. Smell and taste her and occasionally pleasure yourself.
- Squeeze your yoni whenever you can't touch your body, for example, on public transport, in the queue at the post office or during a work meeting.
- Allow yourself to flirt with everyone you meet – men, women and even people much older than you. It doesn't mean that you are cheating on your partner or that you will actually have sex with them. It just allows you to express your playfulness, your femininity and your sensuality in more ways. Flirting is fun!
- Bring the feminine aspects into your daily life. Incorporate emotions, sensations, energy, love, nurturing, expression, juiciness and even rawness and wildness into your studies, career, hobbies, social interactions and spiritual practice.
- Bring sensuality and pleasure into every activity – moan when you eat or when you exercise, touch or caress surfaces and fabrics, smell whatever you can.

The more you express your sexuality, the more your pleasure and orgasm will expand in the bedroom and throughout the day. How else can you express your femininity and sensuality in your daily life?

Now that you are expressing more and more of yourself, it is time to speak up and unleash your true, orgasmic self.

Speak up

Do you express your emotions, needs, ideas and opinions in all aspects of your life? Do you feel empowered to do this with your partner, kids, parents, friends and work colleagues?

Or do you hold back because you fear you will be judged, ridiculed or even ostracized? Do you freeze and feel your throat constrict in these situations? Do you get frustrated afterwards because you wanted to express yourself but couldn't?

And what has this got to do with orgasm?

Well, everything is connected. I have found that many women who have issues with femininity and orgasms also have issues with expressing themselves in public. Some of them also have frequent throat infections. On the other hand, some women who talk a lot actually do this as a kind of protection. They speak about their emotions instead of expressing them. Or they express their intellect rather than their emotions. Or they express their emotions in a way that aims to control and overpower others.

The idea of speaking up is to express yourself whenever you are deeply called to and then allow others to express themselves as well.

If you recognize that you don't express yourself fully, begin by trying to express your emotions, needs and opinions at least three times a day. Perhaps you can share on Facebook, speak up during a work meeting, allow yourself to laugh loudly when you watch a funny movie. Allow yourself to make a request of others, for example, ask your partner to massage your neck and shoulders if you're feeling sore. Or speak up about unfairness at your workplace or about a social wrong.

You could also speak up about your sexuality. One of my clients was unable to talk about her body and her sexuality, even with me when we started working together, for exactly that reason. Yet, after three months of coaching, with my guidance and some work of her own, she became multi-crazily-orgasmic, and was able to talk about her sexuality and even about self-pleasuring with her dildo. She talked about it with friends, inspiring them to work on their own sexuality, and even with men she was dating.

So you see, freeing up your self-expression also frees up your orgasmic experience, and vice versa. When you are able to express your femininity, sexuality, pleasure, pain and emotions in private, you become more able to express yourself in public and in your life generally. And when you speak up and express yourself in your daily life, it makes it easier for you to express yourself even more in private.

Haven't you had enough of hiding, suppressing and gagging yourself? Give the world the gift of you. Share who you really are with others. Express yourself fully. Celebrate your uniqueness and inspire others to express theirs.

Gradually, you will integrate and connect all aspects of your life. You will bring your creativity to your bedroom, your family life, your business and your hobbies. You can bring sensuality and your feminine core to your interactions with others.

When your life becomes an expression of who you really are – you have found yourself.

Unleash it and keep it going!

Sexual energy is what powers your life. It's how you were created, and it's the energy that either charges you or otherwise depletes you if you neglect it or dissipate it. My intention has been to guide you in deepening and expanding your orgasmic experience by yourself, assisting you to become more feminine, expressive and empowered as a woman.

If you have embraced the ideas and practices in this book, you have been on quite the orgasmic journey. You will be aware that you are responsible for your pleasure, healing and growth.

You have read about the difference between clitoral and vaginal orgasms and later about many other kinds of orgasm. You have learned about the huge importance of reconnecting with your body, pleasuring yourself, loving your pussy and expressing who you really are. We've identified different blockages and challenges that can come up on your orgasmic journey and explored a few solutions.

You've learned many practices and techniques to either reach your first orgasm or unleash you full orgasmic power. You have explored different kinds of orgasms and expanded them into long, meaningful, ecstatic orgasmic states.

Finally, you have considered activities and lifestyle choices that will support your orgasmic practice. You now know beyond a doubt that your unleashed orgasmicness, femininity and confidence can transform your entire life.

I invite you to spend some time reading your orgasmic diary and reflecting on how you and your orgasmic experience have changed since you began this journey. Your reflections can be another entry in your orgasmic diary. Not the last entry, but another step on your ongoing orgasmic journey.

I invite you to get up, jump around, make loud sounds and celebrate your achievements. You have dedicated time, moved through challenges, made an effort and now have your unleashed orgasm to show for it. You faced your fears and did it anyway. Well done!

When you make a commitment to yourself – to love yourself and invest in yourself – you always see rewards, and sometimes they are rewards that you didn't even expect.

'When you follow your bliss ... doors will open where you would not have thought there would be doors, and where there wouldn't be a door for anyone else.' – Joseph Campbell

---

So, stay committed to your self-pleasuring at least twice a week. Keep exploring the practices in this book; integrate them into your sex life and your daily life. Re-visit the practices that you found challenging and see how now they are easier, and much more pleasurable. Work on whatever challenges you, both by yourself and with the help of professionals. Finally, make your life an expression of who you are.

Know that there is always more...

Yes. This is just the beginning. As long as you invest in yourself and your sexuality, your orgasmic experience and other aspects of your life will continue to improve over the years. There is always room to learn and expand.

You can always read more books and attend workshops or retreats about sexuality, femininity, relationships, Tantra and personal development. I hold a few workshops each year in Australia, Europe and soon also in the US. To stay updated on these workshops and receive weekly articles about how to express your sexual, creative and business potential, sign up for the mailing list at www.intimatepower.com/orgasm-book-resources. If you would like to organize one of my workshops in your city, please contact me for further discussion.

Also, look out for my *Orgasm Unleashed Online Program.* This program is a charged-up companion to this book, including videos, demonstrations, further explanations and unique topics such as couple practices, special tantric techniques, minimizing the blood loss and side effects of menstruation, and much more. Sign up on the resources section of my website to stay in the orgasmic loop.

I offer coaching, mentoring and guidance to just a handful of business women each year. These women are seriously committed to expressing their sexual, creative and professional potential, and to sharing their gift with the world. Coaching journeys start at $1,000 a month and we can have a single session before committing to a longer process. I offer a $100 discount on my coaching journeys for readers of this book as a token of gratitude and appreciation. For more details, check out the online resources section and feel free to contact me about this special opportunity: www.intimatepower.com/orgasm-book-resources

I would also love to hear from you if this book has served you and if there are other challenges you are dealing with. I invite your feedback and your request for further information or other topics. Connecting with me via the resources section of my website is the most effective manner to do this, so I can respond to you as an appreciated reader of this book.

If this book has inspired you, I hope you consider recommending it to your girlfriends, to young women in your family or community, and even to your male friends so they can learn about their partners. Helping another woman on her orgasmic journey is a beautiful gift to give. Please consider rating or reviewing this book online so that other readers might benefit from it as well. Share the love and orgasms!

I salute you for your commitment and dedication to yourself and to your orgasmic journey. And I thank you for trusting my guidance in such an intimate aspect of your life.

I wish you to be the orgasmic, loving and creative woman that you really are.

With love and many unleashed orgasms,

Eyal Matsliah.

www.intimatepower.com

Extra resources

To access the online resources section of this book, head to:

www.intimatepower.com/orgasm-book-resources

These resources include:

- All of the orgasmic extras and resources that I've mentioned throughout this book.
- More information on "Orgasm Unleashed Online Program"
- A list of recommended articles.
- Recommendations for erotic dance teachers and classes.
- Recommended books.
- An invite to a special Facebook group, where you can connect with fellow readers to hear their inspiring transformation stories and receive support on your orgasmic journey.
- Access to more information about Eyal's transformational workshops.

- How to claim your special discount for Eyal's coaching journeys
- How to stay in the loop about Eyal's upcoming books and online programs about sexuality, personal development and conscious business.
- And much more…

About the Author

EYAL MATSLIAH has dedicated his life to loving and helping women. He has been studying and practicing different modalities of tantra, sacred sexuality, healing, yoga, coaching, and meditation since 2000, and has helped thousands of people all over the world as a sexual healer, coach, author, speaker and workshop facilitator.

He resides in Melbourne, Australia.

LEARN MORE AT WWW.INTIMATEPOWER.COM

List of Diagrams

Printed in Australia
AUOC01n1626280916
279267AU00006B/6/P

9 780994 414915